MANAGING STRESS

I dedicate this book to my beautiful daughter, Zara, who has provided my greatest challenge and given me my greatest joy.

And to all my clients and students who have taught me so much and who give me a wonderful reason to continue to learn.

MANAGING
STRESS

In a Changing World

SUSAN BALFOUR

AURUM PRESS

First published in Great Britain 1998
by Aurum Press Ltd, 25 Bedford Avenue,
London WC1B 3AT

A catalogue record for this book is available from
the British Library.

ISBN 1 85410 448 9

Design by Don Macpherson
Produced by Phoenix Offset Ltd
Printed in China

CONTENTS

Acknowledgements

There are so many friends and colleagues to whom I owe grateful thanks and appreciation for their support and encouragement while I was journeying through the uncharted country of writing my first book. When the path became rocky, Diana Haydon was always encouraging at the other end of the telephone; thank you, Diana. Thank you Francis Kinsman, dearest friend and kindred spirit, for your unbelievable patience and support, and for your belief in me when my confidence faltered, which was often! Thank you Jean Broke-Smith and Christopher Stock for your encouragement and the delicious dinners and essential music which sustained my body and soul, and provided much-needed time off for singing and dancing and for practising what I preach. My wonderful brother, John Pickett, was always available to me when I wanted to let off steam, and so many of my daughter's fantastic group of friends showed constant interest in the book's progress and offered helpful thoughts and ideas: Jasmine Boler, Franziska Thomas, Alex Phelps, Jared Pepall, Richard Marett, Emily Carlisle and Sally McLean – a big thank you to you all.

Enormous appreciation and affectionate thanks go to Amber Lloyd, founder of Relaxation for Living Trust, who started me on the road to understanding the importance of relaxation techniques to combat stressful situations, and amassed the knowledge and skill which I use in my life and work every day. She has taught me – and thousands of others – priceless simple truths. Very special and heartfelt thanks also to two other extremely important mentors in my life, Barbara Somers and the late Ian Gordon-Brown, for their inspiring training in Transpersonal Psychology, for their wisdom, humour and non-judgemental acceptance of all; they have given me the tools and creative perspective with which to do the work I love. I thank and acknowledge Dr Peter G. F. Nixon for his work on which I have drawn for many years, and for generously giving me his time to discuss the stress syndrome and for his papers, as well as supplying the First World War report from the *Lancet* included in the Introduction.

I am very grateful to my literary agent, Charlotte Howard, for her supportive phone calls and her understanding. Grateful thanks are also due to my publisher, Sheila Murphy, for her patience when I grossly exceeded the time deadline, and in editing my over-long manuscript. I especially want to acknowledge, with love and appreciation, John Clifton, who encouraged me to make my first relaxation tape and who always believed in me and the importance of my work. He taught me, by his example, how to persevere and to keep on working at your vision even when the going gets tough thank you, John, for those invaluable gifts. Thank you Anna Cropper for understanding the agony of the creative process, and Anne Leto: your cool wisdom and *joie de vivre* were always sustaining and fun. And finally, I want to thank my beautiful daughter, Zara, for just the right word at the right moment, for challenging me and helping to keep me on my toes, for her good-natured acceptance that sometimes my work comes before her, and for her lovely, quirky humour.

Introduction

What is stress and why do we hear so much about it these days?

A question I am asked repeatedly is: 'Why is there so much talk of stress these days?' People say, 'Hasn't there always been stress, and isn't stress just "life" and having to get through?' And often older people say to me, 'We had just as much stress when we were young, we just jolly well got on with it, without making a fuss!' Well, yes, but...

It is, however, important to ask these questions and to try to answer them, because by doing so we can better understand the fundamental nature of our stress and its causes – and unless you truly understand what it is, you will not be successful in managing it, reducing it or surviving it.

With this in mind, you will find a detailed definition of stress in Chapter 1 and a discussion of responses to stress and symptoms you may have observed in yourself in Chapter 2. These explanations are presented to help you clarify exactly what is meant by the non-specific syndrome we call stress, and to understand a little more about yourself and your reactions. Knowledge conquers fear, so they say, and this book is written out of the desire to expand your knowledge and understanding, and to diminish your fears and anxieties, so that you can become the master of stress rather than its victim. The following chapters then discuss different causes of stress, how to forestall them and, when they do occur, how to mitigate their effects. Throughout you will find useful exercises to help build your stress-management skills.

Awareness of stress is not a new phenomenon; in fact, the beginnings of stress management were developed during the First World War. At this terrible time the effects of prolonged stress on soldiers who had been in the front lines began to be recognised and understood. As a result of their exhaustion and overtaxed nervous systems, a simple, but extremely effective 'sleep therapy' was developed, whereby the strung-out and overstrained returning soldiers were persuaded to rehabilitate themselves by sleeping and resting their nervous systems, with some being sedated into an enforced sleep for many days – sometimes weeks – at a time.

According to eminent cardiologist Dr Peter Nixon, many modern-day disorders, such as chronic fatigue syndrome or ME, Gulf War Syndrome and RSI (Repetitive Strain Injury), as well as cardiac problems, could be better understood by paying more attention to the findings of that early research.[1] Even today, Dr Nixon uses sleep therapy as part of his rehabilitation programme with patients whose healthy function has broken down due to 'effort and distress carried beyond physiological tolerance'. These patients are reacting to life as if they were soldiers 'in the front line', with excessive, unrelieved output; as are many others in life today, who may not yet have broken down but whose current lifestyles are possibly storing up trouble for themselves in the future.

I reproduce the following fascinating report from the doctor treating those exhausted soldiers, which was printed in the *Lancet* on December 30, 1916[2]. This is a perfect description of severe stress syndrome and its management. From this 'sleep therapy' evolved different techniques of relaxation therapy, and stress management was developed to educate individuals to recognise when they are being pushed, or are pushing themselves, 'beyond physiological tolerance', and to train them to return to healthy functioning.

WARFARE ON THE BRAIN.
By E. Farquhar Buzzard, M.D. OXON., F.R.C.P. LOND.

First of all, there are what we may call the pure exhaustion cases. These are men who, starting with an average allowance of resisting power, after a more or less prolonged exposure to the strain of warfare, become restless, irritable, depressed, sleepless, and lacking in attention and concentration. If this condition is recognised in an early stage by the medical officer and rest ordered, a comparatively short

[1] In Suggested Further Reading I include some source material for this research.

period will suffice for the patient to regain his normal health. More often the patient refuses to acknowledge his condition until some crisis occurs in the shape of severe bombardment, an attack of illness, some extra responsibility, or perhaps some personal anxiety or disagreeable incident. Then he is sent home in a more or less advanced condition of "neurasthenia," and something like six months' respite from active service becomes necessary. Naturally each individual has his own allowance of resisting power, and consequently the periods of strain which each can endure vary very considerably...

The proper treatment of exhaustion cases is obviously rest in bed in quiet surroundings. Nevertheless, the patient is generally very reluctant to recognise this, and his feeling of restlessness, often accompanied by a desire for distraction which he regards as the best antidote for his depression, leads him to the opposite extreme, with the result that, unless he is taken properly in hand, he goes from bad to worse and after a month or two at home is much more exhausted than on his return from the front... Over and over again I have encountered dismay and even indignation on the part of the patient for whom I have advised rest in bed as the only remedy for his complaint, and many a time have I been thanked later for my insistence on the advice being carried out.

The common fallacy that lack of sleep at night in an exhausted patient must be met by letting the patient tire himself during the day has to be exposed and explained, and the fact that a sleepless patient suffers little real harm if he is resting in bed often needs emphasising. The prognosis in this class of case is very favourable under proper conditions of treatment, but the period of rest required varies with constitutional idiosyncrasies and with the degree of exhaustion presented when the patient is first seen.

[DEC. 30, 1916, LANCET]

So the phenomenon of 'overload' had begun to be recognised, and it is in this very fundamental concept that we can find the key to answering the question: is there really more stress today than in the past?

In my therapy practice, I see many people suffering from overload: of the senses, the mind, the body, the emotions. Generally, they are not aware of their true condition, they just know they feel tired most of the time and are not coping well with life's demands. This is a widespread condition, and one of the main reasons, in my view, is the size of the context in which we all live. Today's world is much, much bigger than the one with which previous generations had to cope.

And this is the answer to that original question. No, of course stress is not new and of course the size of the actual world hasn't changed, but our awareness of it *has* changed: because of technological innovation and growth in the media, we are aware of, and interact with, much more than ever before. We take in much more than we were designed for and this causes widespread experience of overload, known as stress. The things we have to do in today's world may not be so different from the things people had to do in yesterday's world – we still develop relationships, raise families, earn our living, enjoy our talents, experience leisure and pleasure – but in a significantly expanded context.

In past generations, all the activities of life were carried out in a smaller arena: the local village or small town, or even the large town or city. Up to the beginning of the Second World War, most people's relationships and the things with which they identified were local: people living in Manchester, for example, did not really relate to, or identify with, people living in London – let alone Tokyo or New York.

Today, however, without even thinking about it our context is global – and that is huge! We all wear the same fashions, eat the same food, hear the same news, invest in the same stock markets and fly around the world quite happily and easily. We have become a global community, which, of course, has many positive benefits; at the same time, perhaps we don't recognise sufficiently how extremely demanding, and overwhelming, it can be to have six billion neighbours.

These days, our senses are constantly under bombardment. There are so many more words, images and pictures for our brains to sort through and make sense of. There is a more or less constant demand upon our minds and nervous systems to react to nonstop news and information from all around the globe, often all around the clock. The fax, and many other machines, have little respect for sleep. We are overcrowded by media, advertising, noise pollution, technology and even other people. We are cluttered up with trivia and horror. Before we begin our own day we have usually listened to the news on the radio or television, or read the newspapers, and are so filled with mental activity and emotional churning that we've actually expended huge amounts of energy before we've even started to deal with our own small, personal worlds. Ordinary, everyday life has become almost synonymous with life on the battleground.

Another aspect of this new global context – the awareness of so much more than previous generations had to digest and assimilate – is that there is an overwhelming amount of choice available to us in all of life's different arenas: just going to the supermarket can use up your whole day's quota of decision-making ability, not to mention the strain of choosing which television channel to watch when you finally get home after battling with the rush-hour trains or the traffic jam on the motorway! (This comment is not as facetious as it sounds, because, as I discuss in Chapter 1, we only have a certain amount of adaptive capacity.) No less significantly, we now also have almost limitless possibilities against which to measure ourselves, and against which to fail – a situation which creates high levels of anxiety in and of itself.

So, the phenomenon of size – in all its various manifestations – plays a huge part in the increased experience of stress at this time in humankind's history. In fact, to take this argument one step further, not only is the external experience different, the internal experience is different as well: in being asked to absorb and process many more things than previous generations, we are being required to deal with things for which we were not designed.

I remember John Betjeman – the late Poet Laureate and inveterate commentator on architecture – once saying that the trouble with skyscrapers was that they bore no relationship whatsoever to the proportions of the human body, and therefore we could not relate to them with any sense of comfort. Isn't that true of so much of today's world? It is so out of proportion to us that we feel discomfort with it, we feel overwhelmed by the hugeness and the speed of it. It is not surprising that people experience panic attacks and feelings of anxiety and alienation.

In a way, increased stress can be seen as evidence of a 'design fault': the species was not designed for the environment in which it now finds itself. So the next question is: how are we to handle this incompatibility at the interface between man/woman/child and the modern world? The answer is:

manage it – very seriously.

The truth is, the context in which we all attempt to function is too big, too much, too fast, too polluted, and our capacity to cope is severely strained. Why is there more talk of stress today than ever before? Why is there more subjective experience of stress? Why are there more stress-related illnesses? It is not because we have all become self-obsessed, pathetic weaklings, but because we have not been designed to interact successfully, and with ease (without dis-ease), with life as we are experiencing it at the end of the twentieth century. It is essential that we wake up to the impact this lifestyle is having on our species, a species designed to function optimally in a different context. The design fault, though, is not with ourselves; in fact, we are a perfect design. It is the environment that is the problem.

Somehow, in today's world, as we develop more and more complicated technological innovations that leave us virtually redundant, or at best as only machine operators, we seem to be ignoring the development of ourselves as human beings. In the meantime, we feel ill at ease, threatened, uncomfortable, as if we can't cope – in fact, as if we are being forced to act in a manner for which we were not designed. It is this feeling, this force, that is stress. I have no doubt that in time we will have adjusted to this new world in which we find ourselves (or we will have changed it for the better), but it is now that we feel the incompatibility. It is now that we feel stressed.

But while we cannot change the world (at least not all at once), we can change our reaction to it. We can be in control of how circumstances impact upon us. We are not victims; acknowledging this is the first step in taking control, which in turn is fundamental to stress management.

Stress management is not so much about managing ourselves, as about managing with what we choose to interact: filtering what comes in, discriminating what we allow into our minds and our emotions, limiting what we allow to influence or contaminate us. We have to learn to say 'when', 'how much' and 'no, not now'. Especially 'No!'

All this may sound depressing – but really it is not, because once we have faced the truth, we can do something about it. Denial puts us in the role of victim and makes us powerless; but by facing up to the problem, acknowledging it, assessing it, defining what is going wrong in our lives, having the courage to face the truth and looking at what we need to do to change it, we can make it better – much better.

This book is intended as an exploration, a road map and a guide book. It will explain the specific causes and symptoms of stress, it will provide simple exercises for measuring your own stress, it will show you new methods for solving problems and it will help you develop practical ways to manage your stress. Moreover, it will help you chart a journey into a new way of living your life.

The number-one building block in laying firm foundations for stress-reduced life is: manage the interface. Manage what is coming at you from the outside: limit it to what you can cope with; shape it to dovetail with the resources you have available, rather than trying to extend your resources to cope with everything life demands. Relieve the pressure at frequent intervals. Change your environment to accommodate you, rather than the other way around. But most of all, begin to realise that it is not you who is wrong, it is what is happening in your life that is wrong for you.

We are a perfect design – for a smaller context. Remember, small is beautiful; and although our resources are renewable (the good news!), they are limited. We must learn to husband them; and by doing so, we can become better able to cope in a wider variety of life areas.

Economist Hazel Henderson writes of stress as 'evolution's tool', and adds,

> 'Today we are being stressed to change and evolve as never before. In this sense, the new resource limits and challenges we face are good news. They are stressing us to grow up – to become all that we can be – to discover "the possible humans" that we are.'

But nobody grows all in one big leap; specific steps have to be taken. This book is about those steps. All growth has growing pains attached to it, and we need to manage and limit the pain of growth, so that it does not weaken us; but with care, we can look forward optimistically to the new place we will arrive at, and even to the evolving journey along the way.

Chapter One

Stress – the Specifics and Symptoms

To begin, I want to expand the overview of stress given in the Introduction by defining the problem, how it can affect you and how you can learn to manage it creatively. In focusing on the management of stress, I hope that you will also begin to understand more about certain fundamental principles necessary for health and happiness and for creating a life of quality.

Stress can be understood in the following ways.

Demand for adaption or change

A stressor is anything in the environment – either in the outer world or in your inner environment of mind, body or emotions – that requires you to adapt, adjust or change in some way. Stress is the response your body makes to that demand. There is a limit to how much adaptation you can make or how many adjustments you can cope with over a short period. Try to be aware of how much you are having to adapt at any one time – is it too much, or just enough to be interesting and stimulating, and to stretch you comfortably?

All change is stressful precisely because it requires some adaptation to new circumstances – even pleasant change, like going on holiday, may be stressful if you are already coping with other changes in your life: perhaps a new addition to the family, a house move, a job change or the death of a parent. Everyone has a limit, and if you go beyond that, your adaptive capacity is thrown into overload and can break down so that you feel you can no longer cope at all. At this point even the smallest variation or demand to adapt may be beyond you, and you will resist it.

The 'last straw' could be something very simple, and you might be surprised at yourself for not being able to handle it. So when even small changes or demands make you feel over-whelmed, try to recognise this feeling as a signal that you may be handling too much change and you need time to acclimatise .

Part of managing change is being able to say, 'No, not now!' You might have to tell a few 'white lies' to protect yourself, such as: 'I'd love to come to your party, but unfor-tunately I already have another engagement on that day,' when all you are really going to do is stay at home, put your feet up and watch some undemanding TV for the next fort-night; or: 'I'd love to help at your jumble sale (church bazaar, with weeding your garden, clearing out your attic), but I have an article to finish and I'm already behind with it.' Maybe it's time to let your answering machine intercept telephone calls, because you know you need to escape from the human race for a while. This is especially important if your health, your relationships and your ability to perform are deteriorating.

If you are faced with a large number of unavoidable changes, try to stagger them, or break them up into a number of stages interspersed with time to rest and replenish yourself. Try also to keep as many things as possible the same as previ-ously whilst handling change in only a few areas. One way to monitor stress is to ask yourself if you feel under strain, because when stress becomes strain, then it becomes harmful. As Dr Peter Nixon says: 'It is important to know when to put self-interest before social demands.' Many cardiac casualties are actually victims of themselves, having not learned this les-son, and are, says Nixon, 'dissatisfied by anything less than self-defeating amounts of activity'.

The cross of being a 'Superhumanbeing'!

Being in control of how much change you can handle requires that you develop social skills and tactful techniques (or even low cunning!) to avoid too many demands on your capacity for adaptation when you know the reserves are low. Giving yourself permission to evade demands until you feel restored is one of the first steps in the strategy. Try not to feel guilty if you are not being superhuman. You cannot be 100 per cent adequate 100 per cent of the time, just as you cannot always respond and cope as perfectly as you might wish. So set yourself realistic expectations, and try not to set yourself up by encouraging unrealistic expectations from others, which you then have to struggle to live up to all the time. Allow yourself to be human, which means having limited resources, having occasional 'off' days and sometimes making mistakes.

Managing others

If you are managing others, it is also important to be mindful that if you give people too much to adjust to in too short a time span, they are likely to reject the entire programme, due to feeling overwhelmed. They may not consciously know why they are resisting; they may just feel somehow unable to rise to the demand. Equally, they may well not want to admit that they do not feel up to it, and will find all kinds of rational reasons why the changes are not a good idea. As mentioned above in relation to your own reaction to change: in managing others and trying to implement change, do so in small stages that do not overwhelm people's adaptive capacity.

Keeping track of change

Of course, there are certain times when you have no choice but to go with the flow of the changes that are being demanded by circumstances, but keep a check on them, and take into consideration all the various compartments of your life – home, work and social life. For example:

▲ You may have had promotion at work;
▲ There may have been a restructuring and 'downsizing' in your organisation;
▲ You may have had the builders in at home, so the usual patterns of life there have been disrupted;
▲ You may have been supporting a best friend seriously ill with cancer.

Often these 'life events' cluster all at one time. So, if you feel stretched to your limits, be careful not to make any unnecessary changes – even small ones like altering your route to work or the newspaper you habitually read – as these could add that little extra load that will throw you into overload. And do make sure you have some time to 'coast' – when you do not have to respond or react to any outer demands at all – in order to restore yourself.

Dr Hans Selye, a pioneer and one of the most important researchers of the stress syndrome says:

> It is as though, at birth, each individual inherited a certain amount of adaptation energy, the magnitude of which is determined by his genetic background, his parents. He can draw upon this capital thriftily for a long but monotonously uneventful existence, or he can spend it lavishly in the course of a stressful, intense, but perhaps more colourful and exciting life. In any case, there is just so much of it, and he must budget accordingly.[1]

If you overspend your adaptation energy, you become bankrupt, and there is nothing left over for an emergency. It is essential always to keep some in reserve. Cardiologists like Dr Peter Nixon also emphasise to patients the danger of pushing the body frequently to its limits of adaptation. This puts a great strain on all of the body's internal systems, as it attempts to maintain homeostasis, or balance. He states:

> Biologically, health and survival depend upon the individual's ability to defend the orderliness of his internal systems against the environmental challenges which are high and prolonged in periods of change, uncertainty and turbulence. The defensive forces consist of the homeostatic power of self-regulation and the personal and social skills required for evading or outwitting challenges that might overwhelm homeostatic competence.[2]

Pressure

Stress can also be thought of as the pressure on, or between, parts of an object – a definition borrowed from physics,

[1] From Hans Selye, MD, *The Stress of Life*, rev. edn New York, McGraw Hill, 1976.
[2] See Suggested Further Reading.

17

where it is applied to inanimate objects; but this explanation can usefully be applied to human beings as well. We can take only a certain amount of pressure: just how much depends on how flexible your mind, body, emotions and spirit are, in order to be able to spring back easily from pressures. Obviously, the more rigid and fixed you are, the more easily you may snap or break down in some way when too much pressure is exerted. Being flexible may simply mean accepting things or situations over which you have no control. Fighting such situations as a traffic jam or a delayed train or plane is just a waste of energy, and serves no purpose except to wind you up and wear you out. So practise accepting some difficult circumstances and let some pressures just roll off you.

However, being overly flexible is just as undesirable as being too rigid, as, if you are too flexible, you will be pushed about by others, which will ultimately increase the stress you are facing. You need to acknowledge that you have limits to the amount of pressure you can carry and that when those limits are exceeded you are in trouble. The secret is to relieve the pressure frequently, and not to allow too great an intensity for too long.

Practise becoming more flexible when necessary: for example, when it could save your energy, your health and possibly your sanity. If you give way on less important issues, you will have more strength to hold your ground when it seems essential. Wisdom is knowing when to struggle with something and when to shrug your shoulders and let it go. With each difficult situation, carry out a quick mental assessment, on a scale of 1–10, of how important this really is to you in the overall picture of your life goals. Is it vital enough for you to risk damaging your health? If not, let it go.

Wear and tear

Stress is also the rate of 'wear and tear' on the body. This refers to the body's two metabolic processes: the catabolic, by which we wear ourselves down, and the anabolic, which restores and repairs our bodily systems. We need to find a balance between using ourselves and restoring ourselves – the 'bottom line' as far as stress management is concerned.

Managing stress is about coping with overload and strain,

about being aware when life's demands and challenges have crossed the boundary from being positive to being negative. For even though a certain amount of stress and tension is needed in order to achieve our desired objectives and goals, the 'right' amount can easily tip over into overload without our being aware of what is happening. It is often a gradual process over time, so that we adapt to it without being fully aware of how it is affecting us, and we begin to accept as normal the symptoms of overload:

- ▲ Always in a rush ('hurry sickness')
- ▲ Extreme irritability
- ▲ Extreme fatigue
- ▲ Inability to make decisions
- ▲ Resistance to change
- ▲ Sleeplessness: difficulty getting to sleep at night, or waking in the early hours
- ▲ Non-specific hostility – feeling threatened by life's demands and by other people
- ▲ Loss of a sense of perspective; inability to distinguish between the essential and the nonessential
- ▲ Feeling of being indispensable
- ▲ Reduced resistance to illness
- ▲ Dependence on alcohol, tobacco, drugs or caffeine
- ▲ Digestive disorders
- ▲ Impaired memory
- ▲ Palpitations
- ▲ Excessive sweating
- ▲ Humourlessness

If you experience any of these symptoms, they are warning signals that you are carrying too much stress, that you need to reassess how you are living. Otherwise, sooner or later, something will have to give.

Auditing your situation

Try to carry out a regular, ongoing audit of your life situation to identify which are the most stress-producing areas, which parts cause you problems, and which parts give you joy and satisfaction. The problem parts are the expenditure column;

the joy and satisfaction areas are the income column. What we are aiming for is to make your life as stress-proof, joyful, fulfilling, rewarding, useful and positive as is possible. But first, let's look at the current state of affairs:

	INCOME (plus points)	EXPENDITURE (minus points)

HOME LIFE
- Relationships:
- Distribution of duties *(cooking, cleaning, care of children,dog-walking,shopping, etc.):*

- Rest and relaxation:
- Pleasure
    (massage, sex, long, foam-filled baths, reading for pleasure, etc.):
- Hobbies:
- Entertaining
    (friends, colleagues, family):

RECREATIONAL LIFE
- Sport/exercise/dancing:
- Theatre/concerts/cinema:
- Dining out in restaurants:
- Picnics:
- Walking in parks, the countryside, etc.:
- Creative activities:
- Religious activities:
- Prayer, meditation:

SOCIAL LIFE
- Parties/dinner parties/functions:
- Socialising in the pub, or at your club:
- Membership of groups
    (political and environmental organis-ations, neighbourhood watch, school and charity events,growth groups, etc.):
- Get-togethers with extended family:

	INCOME (plus points)	EXPENDITURE (minus points)
EDUCATIONAL LIFE		
● Learning a foreign language:		
● Study and reading to extend knowledge:		
● Acquiring new skills *(computer skills, car maintenance, cookery, first-aid, etc.):*		
WORK LIFE		
● Job satisfaction:		
● Opportunity for promotion:		
● Relationships:		
● Position in the hierarchy:		
● Degree of control:		
● Workload:		
● Freedom to make decisions:		
● Physical environment:		
● Political environment:		
● Management style:		
● Incentives and rewards:		
● Salary/fees/income:		

Think about how many possibilities there are in each of the different areas of life. How many of these possibilities are you actively engaged with in your own life? Is one part of your life taking up too much of your time and attention, leaving you with insufficient time to reap the potential satisfaction from other areas? If this is the case, think carefully about what you can do to reorganise the balance.

Then on a scale of 1–100 assess your income and expenditure in terms of satisfaction or frustration with each of the areas of your life. Add any other aspects that may occur to you.

Once you have done that, take 50 as average satisfaction, so that anything below 50 counts as a minus, anything above 50 counts as a plus. For example, if you rate job satisfaction at 70/100, that scores you +20 points, i.e. 20 points above 50. If you rate your rest and relaxation at home at only about 40/100, then you score -10, i.e. 10 points below 50. The optimum level is 100, and 50 scores a zero (neither very good, nor very bad – just OK).

How does the balance sheet of your life look? Is there a surplus or a deficit? Are you rich? Perhaps you are richer in some areas that could balance out those where you feel poor. For example, you may be rich in friends and social life, but poor in freedom to make decisions at work.

If the overall picture balances, you can stop worrying about the deficit areas and spend more time rejoicing about the rich parts of your life, and so de-stress yourself by rebalancing your view of your world. It is so easy to take for granted the good things in life and spend most of your time focusing on what is wrong, or what makes you unhappy, thereby contributing to the pressure and the stress. Try to make a conscious decision to count your blessings at least once a day in order to affirm the good things in your subconscious mind. (For much more about this, see Chapter 5.)

Working on the balance sheet of your circumstances should give you greater insight into which areas of your life need some adjustment. You may need to rethink your priorities, so that you can feel a little richer in those areas of your life that may have been neglected and which now appear more important than they did at a previous stage.

A quick technique for managing stress

When you are faced with any stressful situation or life difficulty, ask yourself two questions:

1. Can I change it?
2. Can I accept it?

If there is anything at all that you can do to change things, either totally or partially, then you need to work out a strategy for bringing about that change. Beginning to work on a plan of action for change will make you feel less stressed because you will feel more in control.

If, however, the answer to question 1 is 'No', then you have to answer 'Yes' to question 2 and begin to work on accepting it. This may require changing your attitude towards whatever is stressing you; if that is all you can do, then that is what you must do to safeguard your physical and mental health. We often lack control over events, but we can control our reactions to them, which gives us freedom and a feeling of being in control.

Often, by accepting a situation, you then begin to view it differently, and suddenly become aware of ways to change it. So, by answering 'Yes' to question 2, you may then be able to answer 'Yes' to question 1. Answering 'No' to both questions leaves you in a stalemate position; a hopeless position.

Acceptance does not mean resignation or acquiescence: it means not denying that something is as it is; it releases energy and changes the dynamic so that you often see aspects of the situation that were hidden before. If all your energy is going into resisting something that cannot be changed, you are causing yourself unnecessary strain. Often, when you say 'Yes' to something that you were previously resisting, all kinds of new options suddenly present themselves. Try it, and see how well this technique works. (There is much more about this in Chapters 5 and 10.)

HEALTHY LIFESTYLE HABITS

- ✔ Regular exercise/movement
- ✔ Healthy diet
- ✔ Sufficient sleep
- ✔ Relaxation skills
- ✔ Balance between work and recreation
- ✔ Sufficient fun and enjoyment
- ✔ Moderate alcohol consumption: for pleasure not need
- ✔ Sense of humour

UNHEALTHY LIFESTYLE HABITS

- ✘ Sloth/sedentariness
- ✘ Unhealthy diet
- ✘ Insomnia
- ✘ Tension
- ✘ Workaholism
- ✘ Insufficient leisure/fun
- ✘ Excessive dependence on alcohol and other poisons (caffeine, nicotine, mood-altering drugs)
- ✘ Humourlessness/too much anger

HEALTHY LIFESTYLE HABITS

- ✔ Sense of proportion
- ✔ Ability to lose gracefully
- ✔ Ability to win gracefully
- ✔ Realistic goals
- ✔ Healthy finances
- ✔ Good support systems (family, friends, groups and/or religious or spiritual beliefs)
- ✔ Flexibility of attitudes
- ✔ Satisfying occupation/job/ career
- ✔ Self-esteem
- ✔ Kindness to oneself and others
- ✔ Understanding your stress
- ✔ Knowing how to manage stress
- ✔ Taking responsibility for your happiness

UNHEALTHY LIFESTYLE HABITS

- ✘ Narrowmindedness
- ✘ Resentment of others' successes
- ✘ Arrogance/superiority
- ✘ Unrealistic goals
- ✘ Poorly managed finances
- ✘ Poor support systems
- ✘ Rigidity of attitudes
- ✘ Unsatisfying occupation
- ✘ Low self-esteem
- ✘ Punishing oneself (and having nothing left for others)
- ✘ Denial of your stress
- ✘ Out of control – not managing anything/acting like a victim
- ✘ Blaming others for your unhappiness: expecting someone else to do it all for you

Chapter Two

The Stress Response

Whenever we feel stressed, emotionally aroused or threatened in some way, a series of physical changes takes place within the body. This is called the Fight or Flight Response, or the Stress Response.

As the name implies, this response is designed to help you fight or flee from danger. It is an automatic reaction that will switch itself on before you have had time to think; for example if you step into the road absent-mindedly before realising that a huge truck is tearing towards you at great speed. In this situation, you simply jump back onto the pavement without thinking – an instinctive response short-circuits the logical part of your brain. Or, if someone threatens you in a dark place, you run as fast as you can! You don't think about it, you just act.

When you are in the Fight or Flight Response mode, it is surprising how fast you can run, or how strongly you can fight. The response turns you into a 'Superhuman' who can often perform feats of amazing strength in a dangerous situation because of the chemical changes that take place in the body. This is extremely useful if the danger you are facing is an actual threat to your physical survival, but this response is very wearing and exhausting: it puts you in an unbalanced state because some of the systems in the body are overworking, while others have gone into underfunction. Also, although this response is extremely useful for saving your life, it is of no use in saving your reputation or self-esteem, which are often the threats faced in the modern world.

Nowadays, the problems we face are not usually solved by punching someone on the nose or running away, even though we might often want to react in that way. Sometimes, though, the caveman reaction takes over before the rational mind can restrain it, and people get into fights they often later regret. When we get worked up in situations where remaining calm would be the better solution, we act against ourselves. If we spend much of our waking day in this state (as so many people do, without realising it), then we are exhausting ourselves, wearing ourselves out prematurely and to no avail.

The Fight or Flight Response is an emergency response, meant to be switched on for short periods only, just long enough to get you out of danger. Many people, however, are in this state for too much of the time because they feel threatened by numerous everyday situations. This is a natural and useful response in the right context, but when a physical reaction is not appropriate, you have to learn to switch it off. Here are some examples of how the Fight or Flight Response can work against you:

▲ You may be sitting at home, perhaps in front of the television, thinking that you are relaxing, but you are actually in the Fight or Flight Response as a result of getting wound up about a programme you are watching, or by arguing with the kids about which channel to watch. Maybe they are getting over-excited playing computer games. What's really happening is that you are all working your internal mechanisms as if you were trying to save your lives.

▲ Perhaps you are woken in the middle of the night by noisy neighbours and begin, quite understandably, to feel angry. Your anger pumps adrenaline into your system, making you even more awake and alert. You might then start thinking about some problem at work, and become increasingly alert and wound up. You have switched on the Fight or Flight Response, and the body systems are all geared up for action! But what you badly need is to get back to sleep, so that you will be fresh and rested to handle tomorrow's challenges. What you need to do is switch off the action response.

▲ You may be about to go into an important meeting and are feeling nervous. The last thing you want is a racing heart, sweaty, trembling hands and a dry mouth that can hardly utter a single word. Yet all of those things happen as part of the Fight or Flight response.

What happens to the body in the stress response?

It is important to understand the changes that are taking place in your body when you are under stress, for when you realise how harmful these responses can be if they are left switched on for long periods, you will have the motivation to practise the deep relaxation (see Chapter 3) and other stress-reduction techniques covered in this book.

The heart pounds

The heart beats more rapidly than usual to speed up the blood supply to the large muscles of the body, which are called upon to produce effective Fight or Flight. This is highly desirable in a life-threatening situation, but not much use, and potentially very damaging to health, in less extreme circumstances. Blood pressure is raised, and can lead to permanently high blood pressure if this response is activated too often in everyday life. Angry people tend to suffer more from high blood pressure than those who remain calm in the face of pressures or problems; and in my experience, suppressed anger is the most lethal. Certainly, statistics show that anger is bad for your heart. If your family has a history of heart problems or poor lifestyle habits (see chart on page 23), have regular check-ups with your doctor.

Blood clots more readily, and hormonal and chemical changes occur

Extra blood clotting factors are released to prevent excessive bleeding from a wound. Again, this response is important in an emergency situation, but it is not desirable to have thick, sticky blood circulating round your body every day, as it can lead to the formation of blood clots or possibly to strokes or heart attacks if you already have cholesterol deposits in your coronary arteries.

Extra adrenaline is pumped into the system to keep the Fight or Flight Response going, and although it enhances physical performance, it diminishes the capacity for clear, rational thinking. Adrenaline makes you feel 'high' and 'supercharged', and many people are hooked on this artificial energy which eventually burns them out. Once adrenaline has been kicked into your body, you have to be patient until it has run its course. Try not to get agitated about being agitated, as that will pump out more adrenaline and you will be hyped-up for longer. Just lie or sit calmly and practise relaxing all your muscles, and you will soon calm down.

Extra cortisone is also released from the adrenal glands as a protection against inflammation or allergic reactions, which may be helpful in the short-term, but the long-term effect can suppress the immune system and so reduce resistance to illness. Healing, which depends on inflammation, is also impaired, and ulcers can result from excessive cortisone secretion.

There is an increased output of endorphin – the 'feel good' hormone – which is a very powerful painkiller. However, if the stress response is activated for long periods without respite, it seems that the levels of endorphin are diminished, which may explain why emotional stress can cause us to avoid physical stress, as we instinctively know our threshold to physical pain is lowered.

The supply of sugar increases

The liver releases greater amounts of sugar than normal to provide the extra energy needed to fight or flee from danger. If this sugar is used up in some kind of physical exertion, all will be well, but if it is not, it places a huge demand on the pancreas for extra insulin to facilitate uptake by the body's cells. This can result in breakdown or malfunction of the pancreas, and some doctors believe that diabetes can be aggravated, or even caused, by prolonged stress responses. It is very important, therefore, not to indulge in sugary foods at stressful times – unless you are having to make extra physical effort – as the body is already coping with an excess of sugar.

Excessive sweating occurs

Sweating is the body's cooling mechanism and when faced with any threat this response is heightened to prevent you overheating during a battle, or in running for your life. Of course, in a social or business context this reaction is embarrassing, which adds to one's stress. Try reassuring yourself that your sweaty hands and glowing face could, one day, save your life; this might make you smile to yourself and so relax you, thereby switching off the unwanted adaptation.

Skin turns ghostly white

The colour drains away from the face because the blood supply has been reduced in the surface blood vessels as it is needed elsewhere, and also to protect us from bleeding too profusely from a surface wound.

The senses are heightened

We talk about people 'bristling' with anger or indignation, and this is literally what happens. When we are alarmed, all the hairs on the body stand on end just like a cat's; and although you can't see this reaction, you can sometimes feel a tingling sensation in your skin, especially up the back of your neck. This is a leftover response from primitive days, and is intended to make you look more frightening to an opponent or enemy. However, it is not much use when the enemy is a traffic jam impeding your progress homeward at the end of a demanding day. This reaction makes you particularly sensitive to your closest environment, which is why, when you are in a bit of a state, you probably don't want people too close, and you feel hypersensitive. In fact, all the senses of the body become sharper and more intensely tuned in times of stress.

This heightened alertness is ideal for dealing with an emergency, but cannot be maintained for long periods without respite. After prolonged stress, the senses seem to burn out and become dulled, so that reaction rates slow down. There is a tendency to 'switch off' from the outer world, and this can be mistaken for depression, when it is actually exhaustion from hyperarousal; what is then needed is rest from too much stimulation. Try to be aware of when your reactions have slowed down, as this could be dangerous in situations where it essential to be alert, such as driving a car or using machinery or any other potentially perilous activity like climbing a ladder.

A reduction in libido occurs

The body is extremely pragmatic, and its logic is that if you are in a life-threatening situation, then this is not the moment to choose to procreate or indulge in sexual pleasure, so it shuts down the sexual systems in order to focus the body's resources where they will be needed most to save your life. In other words, sex is superfluous in a situation of great physical danger, and so when you are in the Stress Response there is a predictable decrease in sexual libido.

This can be the cause of many women's failure to conceive, when medical tests have shown that nothing is physically wrong; it can be the cause of impotence in men, or premature ejaculation; and it can be the cause of a decrease in sexual desire. This is why doctors will often say to a worried couple: 'Just relax and take a holiday, and all will be well.' This can be good advice, because in the relaxed setting of a holiday there is more inclination and more opportunity for sexual intercourse. The couple will become more relaxed when away from the usual stresses and strains of everyday life, and so the sex hormones will return to normal levels, and all *will* be well. However, unless this is explained fully, the admonition to 'go away and relax' is not reassuring to people who think there is something seriously wrong with them.

If this is your problem, and you cannot go away, then take a holiday at home. Unplug the phone for the weekend, buy your favourite food and wine, beer or champagne, or whatever you like most – indulge yourselves. Leave all mundane tasks until next weekend and 'play': watch videos, read books, play music and dance together (like you used to perhaps, when the world was young and you were not stressed?); have picnics in bed, and see what happens! Take long, foam-filled baths, preferably together, and perhaps take it in turns to give each other a soothing massage. Just enjoy yourselves unashamedly for a whole 48 hours; you'll probably feel 10 years younger on Monday morning, and this could be the beginning of a whole new way of life. It could certainly be the beginning of family life.

The digestive system shuts down

Once again, the body prioritises against sitting down to eat a meal when you are facing a serious threat, and so the whole digestive tract shuts down either completely or partially. Your mouth goes dry and it is difficult to swallow when you are anxious or frightened; also, you generally lose your appetite. The reason for all of this is that the blood is diverted away from the stomach to the large muscles to give you extra strength and extra speed. The blood vessels to the stomach contract, allowing little blood through, and the digestive juices are diverted elsewhere. This is the cause of digestive disorders like nervous indigestion, nausea, cramps and, eventually, stomach ulcers.

Therefore, it is highly undesirable to eat when you are worked up, as you will not be able to digest your food properly. Try not to eat 'on the run'; sit quietly for a few moments before you begin to eat and try not to have arguments during meals. This latter point is especially important in regard to children: if they become upset at mealtimes, they simply cannot manage to eat or to digest their food fully. So try to avoid battles about eating, and create a calm, happy atmosphere before and during meals. Do not scold children if they do not want to eat when they are upset – they are instinctively right, they simply cannot do it.

Breathing becomes rapid and shallow

This change facilitates a quick exchange of gases – oxygen and carbon dioxide – which in turn increases the performance of the lungs. This is useful when you exert yourself, but not when you sit all tensed up in a state of anxiety, anger or hurt; you may then begin to hyperventilate, which means your breathing is in excess of that required by the activity in which you are engaged, and you may feel dizzy or light-headed, or there may be a tingling sensation in the fingertips, and sometimes in the toes. If you experience any of these sensations – often associated with feelings of panic – you should turn to the breathing exercises outlined in Chapter 3.

Muscles tense for action

It is mostly the large muscles that come into action in the Stress Response: the muscles in your legs and upper arms, the ones that clench your fists and the muscles in your solar plexus to protect against a blow. The shoulders will hunch up and the buttock muscles may tighten, as might the muscles in the soles of your feet and in your toes. An instinctive reaction is to clench the teeth and frown, as this would make you look more frightening to an opponent. It is actually the tension in the muscles that sends signals to the brain via the nervous system and switches on the Stress Response. So sitting at home, or in a train or car, or at your desk with tension in many parts of your body is not doing you any good at all. Although you may think you are doing nothing much, it is actually wearing you out, because all your body's stress reactions are being activated as a result of the tension.

Learning to control the Stress Response

You can switch off the Stress Response by applying relaxation techniques and calming your breathing (see Chapter 3), which will bring the body back to normal functioning and slow down all the internal systems that are racing. Another way to deal with stressful situations is to exert yourself by intense physical activity to use up the extra adrenaline and other stress chemicals, so that the body will then be able to calm down by itself. The following examples should help to illustrate how to use this method:

▲ If you are at home looking after young children who are beginning to drive you mad, run up and down the stairs a few times, or put on some music and begin to dance vigorously, or just jump up and down, encouraging the children to join in. You'll probably all end up laughing, which is the best outcome. Just work off the build-up of stress chemicals in your system.

▲ At work a colleague or your boss winds you up in some way: rather than punching them or hitting out verbally, go into the Flight Response mode and run up the stairs. Or, if that is impossible, find a room some where where you can jump up and down or punch the air, or leave the office and walk rapidly round the block. Work it off in some way in order to calm down. You need to work off the stress build up, and then work out how to *act* – not simply *react*.

▲ Another strategy for releasing tension and stress is to keep cushions handy to scream into or punch and thereby work off a lot of aggression; you can even imagine the cushion is the person you would like to lay into. Shouting or screaming (not at others, but when you are by yourself) is very good for releasing stress because it makes you breathe deeply, which is relaxing in itself. Also, if you do a lot of shouting by yourself in your car or at home with the music turned up to drown the sound, you will almost certainly end up laughing, and laughter is one of life's greatest de-stressors. Try remembering some funny incidents, or imagine your colleagues in ridiculous situations; or just remind yourself of jokes and get yourself laughing.

When people get wound up by daily life, but cannot, or do not, let off steam appropriately, incidents of irrational violence occur. Nowadays, most people's environment and lifestyles do not give enough opportunity for vigorous action, and so unused stress chemicals eventually erupt in violence and aggression. This happens particularly when you are driving: the stress response is being switched on continually as you jockey for position, or when someone cuts in dangerously, or honks their horn unnecessarily. As driving is such a passive activity, eventually something gives, or someone snaps into action in caveman mode, beating the hell out of a fellow motorist. If you find yourself getting wound up and tense when driving, it is a good idea to stop at a service complex, or turn down a side road and walk around for a while to unwind tense muscles and calm yourself.

These are just a few suggestions; the following chapter provides more examples and techniques for relaxing when one is short on time. You do not need to be the victim of uncontrolled Fight or Flight Responses, which raise your blood pressure, alter your body chemistry and burn you out – or worse. You can be in control.

Chapter Three

The Time to Relax is When You Don't have Time to Relax

The ability to relax is one of the best ways to switch off the Stress Response and one of the most important skills to acquire for your stress-management tool-kit. But relaxation is something many people have forgotten how to incorporate sufficiently into their daily lives, as they try to cope with the feeling of being on a treadmill, of having to keep on doing more and more in an endless round to be successful – or just to keep up with the guy next door. It is easy to slide into believing that you cannot take time off to relax, that you must be focused and active at all times, thereby getting more and more wound up in the process.

It is often fear that drives us in this way: fear of being somehow left behind or left out, losing out to someone else, losing our job or not being loved or admired, if we take our eye off the ball for a while. This fear makes it even more imperative to relax when you don't have time to, or when you *feel* you don't have time to relax. When there seems to be no time and space for you, then it is time to take stock of what is happening and *make* time to take the pressure off.

If you relieve the pressure by having regular breaks, then you can take much more pressure in the long term and, ultimately, achieve the success you desire, rather than collapsing, exhausted and burnt out and being forced to take a protracted break that you'd rather not have.

You can push yourself occasionally, but not as a way of life. If you want to work and cope effectively for a lifetime, you must take regular rests. You cannot sprint a marathon. And life is a marathon; therefore, you need to pace yourself in order to survive and thrive during the long haul.

Pace yourself – balance doing and nondoing

Relaxation is passive; tension is active. A tense muscle is using energy and giving off a waste product, while a relaxed muscle is resting, using no energy and causing no waste. Too much tension and not enough relaxation will exhaust you and leave you in a very inefficient state.

True relaxation – and I don't mean distractions like going to the cinema or the pub – happens when your muscles are doing nothing, completely still and resting. In this state the body can replenish itself, as its restorative processes are increased. Medical research indicates that the immune system functions far more effectively when we are in a state of deep relaxation, i.e. with muscles totally resting and with all body systems slowed down. When we are not relaxing, we are using ourselves up; and when we relax, we build ourselves up. This is why relaxation techniques are being taught more widely to patients with serious or terminal illnesses.

In everyday living you should think of relaxation simply as sound energy economics. It makes economic sense to conserve your energy by applying maximum relaxation and minimum tension to everyday tasks.

Maximum work with the least effort equals grace
– Plato

Tension overdraws your energy account

Many people run their energy accounts on permanent overdraft, using up precious energy, even when they think they are doing nothing: like tensing their muscles even when they are asleep. (Therefore, the sleep does not restore their energy loss.) You need to learn (or relearn) the skill of deep relaxation, which is one of the most useful tools for helping you through life.

Tension often becomes a bad habit that creeps up on you gradually, until you literally cannot relax because you have lost the natural ability to let go. You could think of relaxation and tension as two ends of a pole balanced on a central point as shown overleaf:

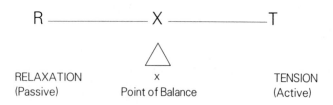

R ——————— X ——————— T

RELAXATION   x   TENSION
(Passive)   Point of Balance   (Active)

Spending too long at either extreme of this pole will put you out of balance. Too much activity and tension is exhausting, and too much relaxation and passivity can cause feelings of lifelessness, stagnation, depression or powerlessness. You may worry that you will never get back into activity if you relax. Sometimes, if you are very tired, you may feel more exhausted after you have relaxed for a while, but this is simply due to getting in touch with what is actually your true state at that time, and it indicates that, in fact, you need more rest. Generally, after a spell of relaxation you will feel released from tension, re-energised and refreshed.

Ideally, we all need a creative balance of both ends of the pole. This does not necessarily mean an equal amount of time at each end, because that is not always possible; but if you have been at the active, tense end for long unrelieved periods and have become severely depleted of energy, then you will probably need an equally long period at the resting, passive end to restore you and put the balance right.

However, people recover their vitality at different rates. The best formula is a little of one, balanced frequently with a little of the other, to keep the balance from tipping too far towards one extreme. It may be worth taking a lesson from the heart: an organ that is designed to last a lifetime. The heart is an 'all or nothing' organ: it is either working, or resting – it beats and rests, beats and rests – and the healthy heart rests slightly longer than it works. Perhaps this is an example for us to imitate if we want to last a lifetime too.

Tension is tiring

Tension is, of course, necessary to perform any action. When we function efficiently, we use the right amount of tension for the job in hand; but when we are feeling stressed or under pressure, we usually tense up tighter and tighter in an effort to try and cope more effectively. Up to a certain point, extra tension can improve performance, but more and more tension eventually becomes counterproductive and results in the feeling of being chronically tired.

A vicious circle can be set in motion: the more exhausted you are, the fewer resources you have to cope, so life can then begin to seem threatening and overwhelming. You therefore tense up more tightly to fight the perceived threat, becoming more depleted the longer this continues. The more fatigued you are, the more life's demands seem like threats; the more relaxed you are, the more life's demands will appear as interesting challenges to your creativity and resourcefulness.

It is vital to learn to cut through the vicious circle and switch off the racing mind and unhealthily aroused body. Unrelieved pressure will sooner or later result in breakdown of either physical or mental health – or both. It may not be dramatic at first, but if you continually push yourself too hard, you will gradually notice that your efficiency level has deteriorated, and you cannot achieve as much as you used to – in fact, everything begins to feel like a strain. This is a warning signal. When most of the things you face each day feel a strain to deal with, you have reached a dangerous level of fatigue, and must take time off to reassess how you are living your life.

What can you do?

Try to become more aware of how much effort you are putting into all the tasks you perform each day. Is it the right amount, or is it too much? For example:

▲ How tightly do you hold the steering wheel when you are driving?
▲ Do you have the right amount of tension in your grip to control the wheel, or are you using more effort than required?
▲ Are you gripping it so tightly that your knuckles are white?
▲ Are you clenching your teeth? We do not need the muscles in the jaw in order to drive a car, but we often use them anyway. We often use more groups of muscles

than necessary for the task we are performing – and this tires us out unnecessarily.

Try to be aware of:

▲ How much effort you use in carrying out everyday tasks: e.g., washing up a mug or plate, washing your self or shaving, opening doors, carrying your briefcase.

▲ How tightly you hold the telephone. Do you grip it as if it were a 10-ton weight?

▲ How tightly you hold the knife to cut a slice of bread.

▲ How many muscles you use when you are keying into your computer. Are you clenching the muscles in your toes, thighs, stomach or forehead? How many unnecessary muscle groups are you using?

▲ Whether you hold your breath when you are listening to a colleague or concentrating on a task.

▲ How tightly you hold your pen in order to control it across the page. Does tightening your grip help you to write faster, or make you more creative? No, it merely tires you more quickly than necessary.

▲ Hunching your shoulders when sitting at a keyboard, or perhaps when playing a musical instrument – or when resisting criticism or other people's opinions.

▲ Frowning or clenching your teeth when playing golf, tennis or board games (or office politics!) Some people grind and clench their teeth when they are asleep.

All of this extra tension is frittering away your valuable energy. Check what is happening in your body right now as you read this. Is there unnecessary tension in your stomach, your solar plexus, your feet, your legs, your neck, your shoulders, your arms, your hands, your jaw? Keep checking yourself, many times each day, so that you gradually become more aware of which parts of your body you habitually hold on to, or habitually hold in tension.

Release tension at regular intervals

The routine outlined on the following pages will help to reduce the tension level from day to day as well as being a preventative measure against burn-out, exhaustion and negative thinking. You can release tension at regular intervals during the day by practising these simple movements that stretch out tightly held muscles. This routine is designed to be used in the middle of a busy day, almost anywhere, to help you to maximise relaxation, dispel tension and conserve your energy. Try them all to begin with, and then pick out the ones that are most useful and work best for you.

These loosening movements and the deep relaxation routine are also given on the tape accompanying this book.

Loosening and stretching

Head movements
- Turn your head to the right, looking over your right shoulder as if you were trying to see someone standing behind you. Feel the stretch on the opposite side of your neck and hold the position for a few seconds, then turn to the left, looking over your left shoulder. Keep your body facing forwards. Repeat six times each side, turning your head as far as feels comfortable; do not strain. Make sure you are not clenching your teeth.
- Tip your head over towards your right shoulder, as if you were trying to touch your shoulder with your ear. Keep your head facing forwards. Hold for a few seconds and feel the stretch in the muscles on the opposite side. Now repeat, tipping your head over towards the left shoulder. Again, hold for a moment and feel the stretch in the muscles on the opposite side. Repeat this movement six times each side.
- Tip your head out and forwards, and feel the stretch in the back of the neck and in the upper part of your back. (This may make you yawn, which is a very good sign.) Now tip your head out and backwards – not too far, as this squashes the upper spine too much. Feel the stretch in your throat and jaw area, and let your jaw hang down loosely.

Repeat these movements about six times each, and always finish on a forward one, so that the vertebrae in the back of the neck are nicely stretched. They become compressed with the weight of the head always pushing down on them, and need frequent stretching and releasing. It is only when the head is supported that the neck muscles can fully relax; so when you are sitting at home, try to have your head supported by the back of a chair, or by a cushion placed between your head and the wall. A head rest in the car is a good idea.

Shoulders

- Circle your right shoulder backwards six times and then forwards six times.
- Circle your left shoulder backwards six times and then forwards six times.
- Circle both shoulders backwards four times; this should leave them less rounded and not hunched up.
- Shrug your shoulders up and then let them drop. Do this a number of times and register what it actually feels like to drop your shoulders. Drop them many times a day. Then pull them down a little further and feel the muscles stretching. Much tension is carried in our shoulders and neck muscles, which is very wearing.

Practise these shoulder movements many times a day wherever you are: in a traffic jam or at traffic lights, for instance. Instead of fuming at what has stopped you, be thankful for an opportunity to unwind and stretch your tightly held muscles.

S - T - R - E - T - C - H

Stretch at every opportunity. If you have been sitting in a static position, at a keyboard, on the telephone, reading, in a meeting, watching television, etc., then have frequent stretches. Stretch out your arms and your hands, especially your fingers and thumbs. Feel how good it is to stretch out muscles that have been contracted for long periods.

Y - A - W - N

Yawn as often as possible! It is very good for you. When the body yawns, it is trying to gain more oxygen. The oxygen we take in when we breathe is our most important source of energy. We can do without food for days, but we can survive without oxygen for only two minutes; yet so many people hold their breath much of the time, or breathe shallowly in their upper chest, and therefore receive insufficient oxygen to support them in their activities.

One way to make yourself yawn is to push your chin down towards your chest and breathe in deeply through your nose, keeping your mouth closed. You will feel a lovely deep yawn beginning in the bottom of your lungs and gradually rising up your chest, expanding your rib cage outwards, until it reaches your mouth and is expelled. Enjoy your yawns!

Breathing

Whenever you have to perform any action or activity that is a bit of a strain, always *breathe out* at the moment of greatest effort. Most people breathe in when making a physical effort, but you should use your breath to assist you, and this is achieved by breathing out – not in, and not by holding your breath. The exhalation gives you extra strength; you have the force of the breath behind the effort. Don't forget to breathe in first, of course, but do not hold your breath as this will increase the strain on the body.

Legs and feet

Stretch your legs and feet if you have been sitting for long periods, at a desk, or in a car or plane or at a meeting. Get up if you can and shake your legs the way you see swimmers and athletes loosening up before a race. If you cannot stand up, then just move your feet about: pull them up towards your knees to stretch your calf muscles, then push your toes down as hard as you can to stretch your shin muscles. (If you suffer from cramp, don't hold this movement for too long.) Stretch your entire leg by pushing your heels away from you. Circle your ankles, first in one direction, then the other, to help your circulation. This should not feel like a chore; just get into the habit of doing these movements all through the day.

Arms and hands

● If your hands have been held in a tense position for a while, bent over a keyboard, holding the telephone or the steering wheel of a car, or while washing up, writing, painting or playing a musical instrument, then shake them frequently, as if you had just washed them and have no towel, so you have to shake them dry

– shake vigorously to dispel the tension. Then stretch the fingers and thumbs out straight, and hold for a second or two. This relaxes the hands very effectively and makes them more supple and dextrous. Do it often throughout the day; do it between tasks.

- To reduce tension in your arms, first shake them the way a swimmer does when limbering up before a race. Feel the shake – the wobble – going all the way up into your upper arm.
- Stretch your arms out either side of your body, and now stretch your wrists so that you push your hands backwards, more or less at right angles to your arms. This is wonderfully releasing if your arms and hands have been held in a fairly static position for some time.
- Swing your arms backwards and forwards rhythmically. Swing them up in front of you to shoulder height, then let them drop – just let them go – and get used to the feeling of letting your arms drop naturally. Keep swinging them for a few moments – up and drop, up and drop – and enjoy this carefree movement. This is a good exercise to do while waiting for the kettle to boil, or standing beside the photocopier or fax machine. Just fit all these movements in amongst your everyday activities.
- Twist your body from side to side from the hips, swinging your shoulders round to the right, then the left, letting your arms swing round as if they were ribbons hanging from your shoulder joints. Let your arms flop and fold round your body at the front and back as they follow the twisting movement. This also feels wonderfully carefree; it is the sort of movement you might see a child doing in the park just for the fun of it. Get back into that childlike sense of being entirely in the present moment, not thinking of what has to be done next, but simply standing and swinging your body and arms.
- Stretch your arms full out and then circle them backwards about eight times; feel how this large movement helps you to breathe more deeply – how your breath feels released from tight bands constricting your middle.
- Circle your arms forwards about eight times: this is

very releasing for your upper back muscles, the muscles around your shoulder blades, and is said to prevent Dowagers' Hump.

Do not keep yourself wound up in action all the time, as it wears you out. Use any annoying situation as an opportunity to remind yourself to unwind. If you are kept waiting by a colleague or your spouse, don't get wound up – stretch and let go. Think of it as putting yourself back into neutral – into a resting state, ready to go into action when needed.

Let irritating situations be your triggers to stretch, unwind and let go. Allow the relaxation response to take over from the stress response – and lengthen your life!

Remember: the stress response affects you more than the outside situation or other people – and the effect is not usually beneficial to your health.

Massage

It is wonderful to receive a massage from someone else, either a professional or one's partner, because massage helps to loosen tightly held muscles so that they can release their waste products. A tense muscle cannot release its waste, which is mainly lactic acid, and if there is a build-up of toxic waste, muscles often feel very sore when touched. It is only when they relax that the waste can be carried away by the increased blood flow – another very good reason to release the tension at every possible opportunity.

Aromatherapy is a particularly therapeutic form of massage because of the wonderfully fragrant essential oils that induce a calm and relaxed state of mind, as well as of body – they really do work.

However, if you cannot persuade your partner or children, or cannot afford to pay a professional, you can do a lot to help yourself by massaging your shoulders and neck frequently, and also your leg muscles, feet, hands and any other bits you can reach.

- Use your fingertips to massage your shoulders, working outwards from where your neck joins your shoulders in a circular movement. Those muscles at the point where the neck and upper back meet are usually very tense and need a lot of massage and easing out. As they release, you should find yourself yawning again. This is a sign that you are getting more relaxed.

● Massage your neck by tipping your head slightly back to release the muscles, then take hold of the skin, squeeze and let go, gently working upwards towards your head. Then, with the fingers of both hands, massage in circular movements either side of your spine, again working upwards from the base of the neck to the base of your skull. Now massage firmly across the back of the head, and slowly work your way up the back of your head, moving the scalp as you go, until you reach the crown. Massage firmly across the top of your scalp, as you do when shampooing your hair. Feel the wonderful release as you move your scalp; this will often unlock tensions in the face as well. You can frequently shift a headache by massaging your head and neck.

● Massage your jaw, making circular movements with your fingertips, letting your mouth hang open. Many tension headaches are caused by clenched teeth, and also by continual frowning.

● Massage your forehead by smoothing outwards with your fingertips from the centre towards the temples at each side. Imagine your forehead widening. Then, gently smooth your forehead upwards from your eye brows to your hairline; feel as if your forehead is getting higher. Imagine all the worry lines are being smoothed away. Tell yourself that your forehead is wide, high, smooth and calm.

● Massage your thigh muscles by squeezing and letting go, and by placing your hands firmly on the tops of the thighs and wobbling the muscles from your groin to your knees. Massage, rub and squeeze around your knees, especially just above the knee where a swelling can sometimes develop. Working around this area helps prevent fluid build-up, which causes the puffiness. Then work on down the leg, squeezing and rubbing the shin muscles on the front, and gently squeezing and wobbling the calf muscles on the back

of the leg.
- A foot massage can be very soothing and will help you to let go and feel at ease with yourself and the world. Gently rub your toes, one by one, especially working around the joints. Rub the soles of your feet with your thumbs in circular movements.
- Massage your hands by rubbing them gently together as if you were rubbing in hand cream, and then with one hand gently rub the fingers of the other hand, one at a time; this feels very comforting.

Deep-relaxation routine

You should try to practise this routine for half an hour every day. It will refresh and restore your body and calm your mind and emotions.

- Lie down on a firm surface, a bed or sofa, or on the floor. Place a small cushion under your head and a large cushion or pillow under your thighs to take the strain off your abdomen and ease the small of your back. Make sure that you are warm, as you cannot relax completely if you are cold. It is a good idea to cover yourself with a rug or blanket, as your body temperature falls when you relax deeply, because your heart rate slows down a little and your blood pressure drops. This is why regular practice of deep relaxation is especially good for anyone who suffers from high blood pressure.
- Become aware of your shoulders and pull them down towards your hips (the opposite of shrugging), hold them stretched down for a few seconds and then let them go. Now feel as if your shoulders are tipping backwards towards the support you are lying on, i.e. the bed, sofa or floor.
- Become aware of your arms. Move your arms a little away from the sides of your body, and bend your elbows slightly outwards. Let your hands rest on your lower abdomen or at the side of your body. Now push your arms down into the support, hold for a moment and then stop pushing. Feel your arms getting heavier.

45

Tell yourself to let go more and more through the muscles in your arms. Feel them being completely held by the support. Let go a little more.

- Now be aware of your hands. With your hands still supported, either beside you or resting on your lower abdomen, stretch out your fingers and thumbs. Hold the stretch for a few seconds and then let your fingers flop. Let them go limp, not holding onto anything, not clasped together, and feel your hands completely still and relaxed. There is nothing for them to do right now, just rest. Feel how calming it is to have completely relaxed hands.

- Now be aware of your legs. Push your legs down into the support – hold for a few seconds, then let go. Now point your toes down, stretching your feet away from you, to stretch the muscles in your lower leg. Hold for a second or two (not too long, as this can cause cramp) and then stop and let your feet flop outwards. Now, let your legs fall a little more apart and let your knees roll outwards. Feel your legs sinking down into the support. Let go a little more. Feel your legs becoming heavier and completely relaxed.

- Now be aware of your abdominal muscles below the waist. As you breathe out, let these muscles feel loose, limp and easy – no holding on. Now feel your buttock muscles letting go. Feel the whole of your lower body being held more fully and relaxing more completely.

- Now be aware of your diaphragm – just above your waist. Feel as if this part of you is expanding slightly. Just let go all around your middle, and feel your easy breathing in this area. Feel your ribcage stretching out wards as you breathe in, and feel your diaphragm expanding. As you breathe out slowly, feel yourself relaxing – feel your body letting go more thoroughly. It is the out-breath that relaxes you.

- Now be aware of your back being supported. Press down a little more heavily into the support, hold for a few seconds, then stop pushing and let go. Feel your whole body being held a little more completely than before. Now let go even more deeply.

- Now be aware of your mouth and jaw. Make sure

your top and bottom teeth are slightly apart, not clenched together. Let your tongue rest on the bottom of your mouth. Let your lips touch lightly. Become aware of how it feels to have a relaxed mouth and jaw.

● Now imagine you are about to smile, beginning in your mouth and spreading out into your cheeks – feel as if your cheeks are widening, stretching out a little.

● Now be aware of your eyes. Close your eyelids, lightly. Let your eye muscles relax – there is nothing to focus on or stare at. Let your eye muscles rest, and enjoy the peace that comes from shutting out all visual stimuli for a while.

● Now be aware of your forehead. Imagine gentle fingers smoothing your forehead outwards from the centre to the temples at either side. Feel as if your forehead is widening. Feel as if all the worry lines are being smoothed away. Imagine your forehead is being gently smoothed upwards from your eyebrows to your hair line. Feel as if your forehead is getting higher. Feel as if you have a high, wide brow that is calm and smooth.

● Now imagine gentle hands are massaging over your scalp: up over the top of your head and down the back of your head. Feel as if your whole head area is expanding a little. Let go through all the muscles in your scalp. Relax your scalp and head.

● Now just enjoy the feeling of being relaxed. Enjoy the feeling of ease. Rest in the feeling of calm that comes with letting go.

● Stay with this relaxed feeling, and rest your mind by picturing a beautiful, peaceful place – somewhere you would like to be right now. Rest in this beautiful place in your imagination for a few minutes. Enjoy being there and taking a little time away from the outside world. Be aware that this is a very healthy thing to do. You are not wasting time – you are using time very creatively to restore your energy and vitality.

● Hold the awareness that all the repair processes of the body are enhanced and the immune system is boosted, when you are in this state of deep relaxation.

● Half an hour is an ideal time span for this deep, restorative relaxation. When you wish to come back

47

into normal alertness, do so gently and slowly. First, gently wiggle your fingers and toes; then, have a gentle stretch – stretch out your arms, fingers, legs, feet and toes. Push your heels away from you to stretch out your spine and body. Roll onto your side and sit up slowly, as all the systems in the body have slowed down and you do not want to shock or strain them. Just sit still for a few moments, taking plenty of time to return to your normal, everyday awareness. Then stand up slowly, so as not to feel dizzy; and try to move and speak a little more slowly than you usually do for as long as you can. Just keep that feeling of calm with you for as long as possible.

Five-minute breathing exercise

This exercise is intended to restore you to feeling calm and at ease when you don't have time to practise the deep-relaxation technique.

This routine can be practised sitting or lying down – if you are sitting, sit well back in your chair, letting the back of the chair support your spine, with your legs uncrossed and both feet on the ground.

- First, breathe out; let your breath out in a slow sigh. Now breathe in slowly, feeling your diaphragm (just above your waist) expand outwards. As you breathe out again, say to yourself: 'Let go,' and feel yourself beginning to release the tensions in your body.
- Now breathe in again, feeling your ribcage expand sideways, on either side of your body, and then slowly exhale, letting your out-breath be a little longer and a little slower than your in-breath.
- Repeat by inhaling slowly. Experience your ribcage spreading sideways and your diaphragm expanding in the front of your body. Never hold your breath once you have inhaled, just let your breath out again in a slow sigh. Pause for a second before you breathe in again, as above, feeling the expansion in the middle of your body.
- Continue this rhythm for about five minutes.

Concentrate on making sure that you are breathing into the middle of your body, feel that part of you expanding sideways, and let your out-breath always be a little longer and a little slower than your in-breath.

- Practise at first by counting to three as you breathe in, and to four as you breathe out. Do this by saying slowly to yourself as you inhale: 'In, two, three.' Then, as you exhale, say: 'Out, two, three, four.' Continue for about five minutes. This counting is simply to give you the experience of breathing out for a little longer than you breathe in; but if it feels wrong, forget the counting and just focus on slightly lengthening your out-breath.
- Practise this exercise every day, a number of times a day, so that when you actually need it, you will be skilled at calming your breathing and bringing it down to your diaphragm, where breathing is designed to take place for ordinary, everyday activities.
- Use this technique to re-establish equilibrium after, or during, any stressful event, or after a difficult encounter with another person.
- When you have mastered your breathing, try to imagine that you are breathing out any negative emotions you are feeling. Visualise them floating away, and then breathe in positive emotions, to calm your inner state. For example, breathe in calmness and tranquillity. Also breathe out attitudes that are no longer relevant or useful to you; breathe in an attitude that would be more helpful. For example, breathe in an attitude of tolerance, patience, stability or centredness. (For relaxation techniques for the mind, see the end of Chapter 5.)

Remember an ancient Yoga saying: 'When you can control your breath, you will control your life.'

Chapter Four

Take Good Care of Yourself

This chapter looks at the many ways in which you can build your resources, enhance your wellbeing at all levels and maximise your resistance to ongoing stresses, as well as to those unforeseen ones that can occur at any time.

People often feel unable to cope well with stress because they are not living fully enough and have allowed their life to narrow down to just one or two areas, perhaps work and home, or even just work, and are ignoring all the other possibilities life has to offer. This sounds paradoxical, for when you feel stressed and overstretched you may think that taking on anything more is the last thing you need. But often doing something different means that you express another aspect of yourself, which can be surprisingly refreshing and rejuvenating, giving you more energy and enthusiasm for everything else. Functioning too much out of one side of your self – say, your serious intellect – will make you feel diminished and constricted if you have no opportunity, or do not allow yourself, to balance this with some humour and light-hearted fun, or some physical or creative activity.

Another imbalance may be that you are giving out all the time, for instance if you are a mother, a teacher or a performer, or if you are responsible for managing a large number of people. You need then to weave into your schedule more activities that replenish you, in order to avoid feeling 'drained' or 'played out'. When we begin to feel stale, dull, not quite well, unenthusiastic – definitely below par and not on top of things – it is often a sign that we have allowed life to become narrow and have suppressed some of our needs. If you find yourself feeling like this, try to listen inwardly to the parts of you that are dying from insufficient use. One way to gain insight into what requires attention is to recognise when you feel envious or resentful of some aspect of another person or their lifestyle; this is often an indication that you feel deprived of similar things in yourself or in your life.

Friends can usually see what stressed people are doing to themselves; but it's not always so easy to recognise what we need to change and what we need to do for ourselves. Other people may suggest things that deep down you know are right – that you are taking things too seriously lately, that you need a holiday, a break from routine and deadlines, time off to 'play', to take vigorous exercise or just to dream.

Your partner might complain that you are becoming irritable and intolerant, and you might feel that you need to expand your life. Sometimes life itself will take matters in hand and present you with a fateful occurrence, like redundancy or a promotion, which forces you to develop your resources and polish up unused skills and talents.

The point I want to make is that, as an adult, you must be responsible for taking care of yourself if you want to thrive. We are all conditioned by early life experience to expect someone else to take care of us and, as we tend to revert back to instinctual modes of behaviour when stressed and under pressure, we often abdicate responsibility for aspects of our wellbeing, unconsciously waiting for someone to tell us what to do or when to stop.

You may have a partner who looks after you, but there is a danger that you then go along with what someone else thinks you need, rather than working out for yourself what would truly make you happier, healthier and more fulfilled. Also, if you are relying on your partner too much, you can fall into the trap of blaming him or her when you don't feel on top of the world. We all have a tendency to look around for someone to blame when things are not as we'd like them to be, even if it is only ourselves we blame. By not moving on and working out a strategy for getting more of what we need – or want – we are missing the point.

We all need to feel valued, and taking care of yourself is a way of acknowledging that you are valuable. You may be feeling stressed precisely because you have not been taking care of yourself adequately. You may have got into bad lifestyle habits, which might have been necessary at one stage to advance your career but which are now inappropriate. There are, of course, times when you must be single-minded and focused on one area of your life to the exclusion of others: when taking exams, working for a degree, training for a sport or important performance, or working against a tight deadline. But this narrow focus must not be allowed to go on for too long without reappraisal. If we become too 'one track' for too long, we become dull and depressed. In my view, depression *is* suppression: a feeling of being constricted or paralysed. There is a very apt saying: impression without expression leads to depression.

When genuine needs are identified and met, people feel less stressed; but because people are often out of touch with their real needs, they create artificial ones that do not truly satisfy. Therefore, if you feel dissatisfied much of the time, this could be an indication that some genuine needs are being ignored, that what you once needed is not satisfying you any longer and that you might need to alter your priorities now. So, consider for a moment how wide or narrow your life is:

- ▲ What do you do in the week?
- ▲ What do you do at weekends?
- ▲ Would you like to do more?
- ▲ What would you like to do differently?

Write down what else you would like to do, no matter how crazy it may seem. These are the neglected parts of you speaking. How can you accommodate them more fully? Do not just shrug off whatever you want to do more of or the talents that you would like to develop – take yourself more seriously.

Looking after yourself and giving yourself what you need gives you a sense of being in control – of being 'The Boss'. Think of it as being the Managing Director of Me Ltd. What does Me Ltd need in order to function at the most productive and optimum level?

Make another list of what is required in order for you to Feel Your Best, Do Your Best and Think Your Best. You may think that, without more time or money, these things are out of reach or beyond your control – that it is just not possible for you to do what you want or need to do. The important point, however, is that we all make choices about how we use our time, or how we earn and spend our money. It may be that you should be re-evaluating how you spend your life.

You may not be able to change things all at once, but just start by making a few changes, putting one or two new activities into your schedule. You will be amazed at how much better you feel – how much more relaxed you are. Just take a few steps at a time.

For instance, a recent client courageously started taking singing, guitar, and tennis lessons at the 'ripe old age' of 39. As a young boy he had showed artistic and musical promise and was exceptionally good at sports, but these activities were gradually squeezed out of his timetable as he focused more and more exclusively on gaining good academic results and eventually a degree in law. He had come to see me because of panic attacks, feelings of extreme anxiety, sleeping difficulties and worries that he would not be able to continue to hold down his highly paid and demanding job.

As we worked together, he began to realise that he had allowed himself to narrow down to such a degree that he was boring even to himself. He felt inadequate with many of his colleagues, who were more versatile and talented, especially on the golf course and the tennis court. And so we worked on helping him to rediscover the talents he possessed. He has become calmer, happier and more in control of himself as he has opened up channels to his artistic and sporting sides. He is using more of himself, doing more and yet feeling more full of energy and enthusiasm.

A by-product was that, as other areas of his life opened up, the stresses of his job appeared less overwhelming. He forgot about the problems at work while he concentrated on learning his new skills, and so he came back to work mentally refreshed. He stopped worrying about the future and began to enjoy the present, to sleep well because of the exercise he got playing tennis. The singing lessons helped him to breathe correctly and fully, and relaxed many of the tense muscles in his chest and shoulders.

Your personal inventory

Giving yourself what you need is not selfish. It's just the reverse. If you feel needy and depleted, you will not be able to give very much to your job, your partner, your children or your friends. Consequently, you become less interesting and rewarding to be around, so people avoid you, and this makes you more needy.

So, how do you begin to understand what you really need? I suggest that you work out in more detail just exactly where you are right now by using the satisfactions/frustrations chart below to evaluate the different areas of your life. Under the appropriate headings, list your satisfactions and frustrations about each. I call it a Personal Inventory.

	SATISFACTIONS	FRUSTRATIONS
WORK:		
HOME:		
FAMILY:		
INTIMATE:		
FRIENDS/ SOCIAL LIFE:		
HOBBIES/ OUTSIDE INTERESTS:		
FINANCES:		

Take time to reflect on what you have written down. This chart gives you a picture of the status quo, of how things are right now in your life. It is an indication of what your feelings are telling you about your current lifestyle. This may point towards what else you need to round out your life.

Often we suppress our feelings and do what we 'think' we should do even if it doesn't 'feel' right; somehow we relegate our feeling nature to an inferior position. If this happens too often, sooner or later something snaps and our ability to cope is undermined. The Personal Inventory chart can be used as a reminder about what needs to be worked on, and can be referred to regularly to keep a check on how things are progressing. Use the chart to get in touch with aspects of yourself you are not expressing sufficiently. Try to identify which areas give you the most frustration or distress:

- What does your logical mind say about these problem areas?
- What do your emotions feel about them? Try to create a dialogue between your thoughts and your emotions.
- What does your body say about your current habits – is it happy, healthy, fit, energetic, free from aches and pains? Try to get in touch with it.

Your different sides

As human beings we consist of body, mind, emotions, soul and spirit, all of which need to be nurtured, nourished and expressed appropriately. When any part is ignored or neglected, we become less happy, satisfied and relaxed. So try to be aware when one part of you is stifled or overused. Let's begin by looking at what is required by the mind, the emotions and the body, as they are the easiest to comprehend and deal with; the other aspects will be addressed later. Think of yourself as an equilateral triangle, with each side representing an aspect of you, like this:

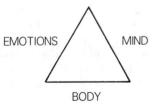

Each of the three sides must be cared for equally in order for you to function at an optimum level. If one side is under strain or neglected and another dominates, after a while this unbalanced state will begin to affect your coping capacity. Maintaining balance and being relaxed and on top of things is most possible when all your aspects are allowed expression and given due attention and care.

The aspect that we often value more highly than any other is the mind, which dominates the agenda while the emotions are undervalued and suppressed, and the body is often ignored completely. The mind says, 'You must achieve such and such,' while the emotions say, 'I'm scared! I might fail; I might be made to look stupid; maybe I'm not up to it.' The mind overrides the emotions, as they are getting in the way of its aims, and the body, so often caught in the crossfire between the mind and the emotions, goes into seizure as a result of the inner conflict. The emotions have been dismissed by the rational mind, but they are still around, and their energy is trapped in the body. It is not difficult to see how this can lead to physical problems, such as aching muscles, tension headaches, raised blood pressure, spastic colon and so on.

Taking care of your emotions

What is needed is to acknowledge emotions, not suppress them, even if they are inconvenient and not what you are 'supposed' to be feeling. Emotions, or feelings, can be divided into two categories: negative and positive. It is usually the so-called 'negative' emotions that we deny, reject or suppress: feelings of anger, fear, sadness, depression, worthlessness, shame, grief, lack of confidence, insecurity and so on. These feelings are perfectly legitimate, and it is in denying them or being ashamed of them that we do ourselves damage.

You can stop your emotions sabotaging you, or bursting forth in an unexpected overreaction, by just saying 'yes' to them, experiencing them inwardly and, if possible, expressing them in some way outwardly, perhaps verbally, by writing them down, or in some other physical way. Because emotions are active, they should be actively expressed. Just find some way to acknowledge to yourself what you are feeling. You don't need to admit it to anyone else, unless you want to. But do not criticise yourself if emotions sometimes affect your performance in life. Self-acceptance reduces tension between your different parts and makes you more relaxed, which will always improve your ability to function well.

Once you have acknowledged that you are feeling a particular emotion, you will experience a renewal of energy where before you felt fatigued from the effort of denial. Our emotions are the truest part of us and, if listened to sympathetically, they rarely lie; they often make the most honest statement about our position. Of course, emotions are sometimes inconvenient for the mind's game plan, or for someone else's comfort. But even though 'negative' emotions cannot always be expressed in every situation, they should be listened to and nurtured. Ignoring messages from the emotions causes inner tension and constricts the whole personality – all of which will eventually lead to adverse physical symptoms.

Negative emotions, such as anger or hurt feelings, are usually a sign that certain needs are not being heeded, either by yourself or others. If you do not listen to yourself, then it is very difficult to get other people to listen to you, because you are not in touch with what you need from them. How can others take your needs seriously when you do not?

Denial of what you feel may of course stem from your emotions being unacceptable when you were young, so you may have to retrain yourself to accept that you have a right to have your feelings taken seriously, both by yourself and others. Sometimes it is hard to acknowledge vulnerability, weakness or need. But we are all vulnerable, weak and needy at times, and to deny this fact is to deny part of our human nature, and is not useful, helpful or healthy. In fact, it is very unsupportive of yourself, and adds to your overall stress.

Sometimes the emotions dominate – perhaps because they are in turmoil – making it impossible for the mind and body to function adequately. They may then need rational arguments or cool logic to demonstrate that things are not as bad or as uncontrollable as imagined. We can often bring emotions into greater balance by thinking things through rather than feeling things too acutely.

Remember, the mind and the emotions need to work in partnership with the body as their support.

Taking care of the body

Some people deny and ignore their body, treating it as if it were little more than a sort of hat-rack for carrying the head about. If the mind is allowed to dominate, it will ignore the signals from the body, dragging it on and on until the desired objective is achieved, depleting the bodily systems in the process. The intellectually dominated person may often feel disembodied, preferring not to give much attention to the body's needs; but the mind does not function optimally without the co-operation of the body, and must sometimes defer to the body's need for replenishment. The body must be given equal time and equal care in our daily schedule for it to be as healthy as the mind and the emotions. Two significant needs of the body are exercise and, even more importantly, sleep. (Correct diet is assessed in Chapter 6.)

Exercise

The body, of course, needs regular exercise, and exertion is an ideal way to work off the tension that builds up through the frustrations of each day. Exercise also helps the breathing to deepen and descend to the diaphragm. This increases the supply of oxygen to the brain, as well as causing the release of the 'feel good' hormone endorphin.

If you dislike organised exercise, simply try to fit more movement and exertion into your daily schedule. For example, walk or run up stairs instead of taking the lift. Get off the bus or train one or two stops earlier and walk the remaining distance to work or home.

The new thinking about exercise is that it is not ideal to 'work out' in short, intense periods, but that it is healthier to increase general exercise during your day, in an ongoing, gentler way. So use every action you perform as an exercise for the body: stretch a little more as you reach up into a cupboard or a shelf, or down towards floor level. Put on music at home and dance; go ice-skating or horseback riding with your kids; or just walk more – a brisk walk for twenty minutes a day is excellent exercise. (See Chapter 3 and the tape that accompanies this book for loosening and stretching movements you can use anywhere, to de-stress the body.)

Nevertheless, however important exercise may be, it is not

wise to push a tired body. Never suddenly start vigorous exercise after months or years (or decades) of non-activity. Build up your fitness gradually, and always remember to warm up gently at the start of exercise and to wind down gently at the end. If you are exhausted, then first you need rest and sleep to replenish your resources, after which you can start getting fit.

Sleep and how to induce it

Despite its pre-eminent importance in maintaining physical, emotional and spiritual equilibrium, sleep is often the first thing to be sacrificed, because the emotions will not be quiet or because the mind is focused on achieving its goals. Here are some techniques for improving your sleep:

- Protect yourself against too much light. Your eyes do not rest well if light is present, in fact, they send very slight, but nonetheless stimulating impulses to your brain. Therefore, you might try wearing an eye mask. If complete darkness makes you anxious, have a light on outside your door, but preferably not in the room itself. You could also buy one of those little night-lights that plug into a wall socket and produce a low glow.
- Protect yourself from as much noise as you can. Fit double glazing to windows; have thick curtains to absorb sound; choose a room away from the road; insert earplugs. If, however, in spite of all precautions, noise is interfering with your sleep, try not to tense up against it. Rather than resisting, listen to it and say 'yes' to it. Practice relaxation and breathing techniques, and eventually you will find you can drop off to sleep even in the midst of loud noise, as children and babies do.
- Ensure a comfortable temperature in your room; eliminate draughts. Experiment to find which temperature makes you feel most peaceful and comfortable. I prefer my room to be very warm – it makes me feel as if I am held in a warm security blanket. So, each to their own, but don't be bullied by others into doing what doesn't feel right for you. This, of course, applies to everything in life.

- Give yourself time to unwind before attempting sleep. Do not undertake just before bedtime tasks that might stimulate your mind and which you cannot complete. If you do, your mind will keep on struggling with the problem all through the night. The same applies to reading before sleep: if the book is stimulating, you may find it wakes you rather than soothes you.
- Try to gently disengage your mind from the day you are leaving behind. Soothing music may help to slow you down, as may a warm (not hot) bath with relaxing bath oils like lavender or jasmine.
- Don't do any vigorous exercise or strenuous physical work just before retiring, as this will speed up your heart rate and other systems just when the body needs to slow down.
- Lack of calcium is thought to be a contributory cause of sleeplessness, hence the milky drink at bedtime, but if you don't want to take milk due to allergy or concern about weight increase, then try a mug of camomile tea, as camomile is rich in calcium and quite soothing.
- Practise relaxing all through your body when you get into bed, just saying to each part in turn 'let go', and as you let go, breathe out in a gentle sigh.
- The best technique of all, which almost always works for everyone, is to focus on the rhythm of your breath, ensuring that your out-breath is a little longer and a little slower than your in-breath. Breathe low into your abdomen, feeling the middle of your body expand as you breathe in, and then experience how you sink down a little more each time you breathe out slowly.

To return to the model of the equilateral triangle: the body and mind need to be *exercised*, fed and rested; and the emotions need to be *expressed*, fed and rested. If you do not heed your various sides, you are working against yourself and functioning as a poorly managed organisation does when different departments work against each other, rather than in co-operation.

Maslow's Hierarchy of Needs

When discussing which needs are important for optimal well-being in therapy sessions, I frequently use Abraham Maslow's Hierarchy of Needs as a starting point. Maslow, one of the founding fathers of Humanistic Psychology, maintained that, unless the first three basic human needs are adequately met, one cannot realistically aspire to the more ambitious levels (see below). When the basic survival needs are not met, all one's energy will be directed towards satisfying them: a starving man's thoughts are wholly directed towards obtaining food rather than improving his mind. So, in order to take the next step in development, one must first sufficiently fulfil the previous need.

As you consider each sequence of Maslow's hierarchy outlined below, try to register your feelings, which will indicate – more truthfully than your mind or rational side – how well your various needs are being met.

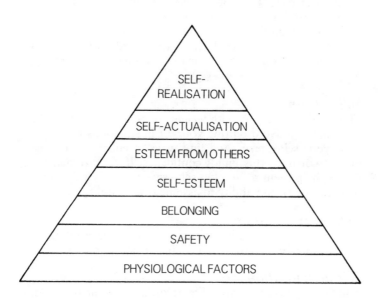

Physiological needs
These, of course, are the bodily needs for food, drink, sleep, rest, warmth, shelter, sex, movement, cleanliness, etc.

Safety
This relates to the emotions; if we feel unsafe or insecure we cannot function optimally. This need is especially important in learning situations: fearful children or teenagers cannot learn well or apply themselves to creative activities. The need for security should also be recognised in any context where one is managing others. To be effective, a management style or company culture should be based on an atmosphere of encouragement, appreciation and trust. If people fear that they will be penalised for getting things wrong or making a mistake, they will stick to the tried and tested and never go any further – and will thus be less than optimal employees.

Belonging
We all need to feel we belong somewhere, whether to our family, our friends, a club, a religious group, a profession, or the organisation where we work. If you feel isolated, try to find some group that can take care of this fundamental human need for affiliation: ideally, one associated with an activity that interests you, perhaps amateur dramatics or some type of sport.

Self-esteem
This need is bound up with feelings of personal respect. Make sure that you avoid putting yourself in situations that undermine your self-esteem, and find ways to enhance your sense of self-worth, as this builds confidence. If you are managing others, help them to develop self-esteem, as this will increase their creativity and ability to assume responsibility.

Esteem from others
This need interacts with self-esteem, as we need positive feedback from others to support a confident view of ourselves.

Self-actualisation
This involves running your life according to your own script, standards and values. It relates to a state of freedom and

authenticity which incorporates responsibility and awareness: doing willingly what you have to do. This highly developed individuality is, in fact, the secret of success. Obviously, in order for this state to be achieved, all the preceding needs have to be fulfilled.

Self-realisation

This is a state of spiritual awareness of your true nature – of your Spiritual Self. This is also called Individuation, being aware of your Higher Self. It is what Jesus meant when he said, 'The Kingdom of Heaven is within'. It is also what Buddha called 'Enlightenment'. Some people maintain that the purpose of life is to arrive at this point, that all the other levels are simply stepping stones to this ultimate destination.

Balance head, heart, and will

Another helpful model is to think of yourself as having a threefold nature of Head, Heart and Will, or Thinking, Feeling and Willing. In order to be balanced, each nature must be expressed appropriately. Examples of balanced Head, Heart and Will can be related to various occupations:

- If, for example, you work exclusively with your mind and intellect during the day, try to express your artistic, emotional nature during leisure time. Or engage in some sport or physical activity that would use your will, which is said to reside in the limbs and lower body.
- If your daily work is physically demanding, then in the evenings or at weekends you need to exercise your mind, perhaps by learning a foreign language. Or, you could try finding an outlet for your emotional and artistic self, perhaps by writing, singing with a choir or learning to sculpt, paint or play a musical instrument.
- If your work makes great demands on your emotions or your 'heart', like working in any of the caring professions, or indeed working as an artist, musician or actor, you might need something purely physical like dancing, swimming, or yoga to balance and refresh you.

Whichever part of your self needs attention, meditation is a wonderful way to calm, restore and balance all of your nature and to bring you into a feeling of inner harmony.

Another way to get in touch with what truly nourishes you is to ask, as Barbara Somers says, 'What makes my heart sing?'[1] Think about this question carefully, feel it fully and then write down your response – and keep whatever you have written with you always. It is a touchstone to your authentic self, to the original and individual human being that is you.

You may be feeling confused about the words 'soul' and 'spirit', and wonder how one meets their needs and what the 'soul' actually is. My definition is that the soul is our higher feelings, those that are not exclusively personal nor to do with our everyday lives. They are altruistic, uplifting feelings of compassion, joy and ecstasy. And in my view what feeds those feelings, or what feeds our souls, is culture. In its myriad forms – art, music, dance, sculpture, poetry, literature, architecture, language – culture is the expression of the abundance of human creativity, and its purpose is to remind us of our true nature and of human possibilities. When you consume culture, or engage in an artistic activity, you feed your soul. Of course, the beauty of the natural world uplifts the soul and the spirit too. The spirit is fed when you awaken to an expanded dimension, when something opens up the perspective to something greater than yourself and the ordinary, everyday view of life.

Discover for yourself what nourishes and cares for your spirit and soul – do not neglect them. See Chapter 10 for more on this.

You may have wondered why the need for love has not been mentioned – and quite rightly too. The need for love is often thought of as our greatest need, indeed, as our only need. Certainly, if we are going to take care of ourselves, we need to find love. However, if you are starving, or if your life is in danger, is it more important to find food/safety or love? Your basic need at any particular time is the most important need, and until that is satisfied, nothing else can be.

The point is that the more of these needs you meet, the happier, more fulfilled and less stressed you will be. This is the way you love yourself – the most fundamental kind of love from which all else grows.

[1] See Acknowledgements.

Chapter Five

You Are What You Think

'There is nothing either good or bad,
but thinking makes it so'
Hamlet (Act 2: Scene ii)

The power of the mind is enormous, and this power can be used to support you or undermine you. What you think shapes your life, and the ability to manage your thinking is a very important component in the successful management of stress. Recent research shows that how you evaluate what happens to you, or how you interpret a stressor, can be a decisive factor in whether something is stressful or not.

There is an ancient Chinese saying: 'As a man is, so he sees,' meaning that one sees through the lens of whatever is within: how we relate to the world is coloured by what is already in our mind. Therefore, how we see things says more about what is in our mind than it does about the outside world. A difficult concept to come to terms with, perhaps, yet how often do we challenge the programming of our mind? Is it correct, or does it need a little adjustment? This usually happens only when we are facing a crisis of some sort and are forced to question or reconsider our mental position. Every crisis, therefore, presents us with an opportunity to rethink the status quo, and to make adjustments where necessary. In fact, it is worth noting that crises often occur *because* we are malfunctioning in some way: there is an error somewhere that needs to be dealt with. If we can approach crises in this light, they can be viewed positively as a chance to correct the errors in ourselves and in our circumstances. When facing a particularly stressful problem, you could ask yourself, 'What needs changing here?', because crises, stressors and difficulties, whether at work or at home, can often only be resolved when we look at things from a new angle.

What is really going on?

Therefore, when something in your life feels very difficult, upsetting or stressful, if you can change your thinking and turn your attitude around, it may begin to feel less so. If something looks 'bad', try to turn your thinking around and find some 'good' in the situation. This might sound rather Pollyanna-ish (the girl who always looked for the good in everything that happened to her), but why not? This way of looking at things dilutes the negative aspects by adding some positive to the total picture. You begin to bring equilibrium into circumstances which may previously have had you feeling off balance and somewhat overwhelmed. It's not a question of deceiving yourself about problems or stressors – simply that you discipline yourself to look for ways to think positively, which will empower you.

When we are particularly stressed, pressured or exhausted, our thinking often turns negative and gloomy. Our bodies get tight and constricted, and our thinking becomes narrow and unexpansive. We *feel* we can't cope and we *think* we can't cope, and eventually we make this a reality: even if it is initially untrue, we bring it about because we look for evidence to support our way of thinking.

But by shifting perspective and trying to think from another angle, we can usually find evidence to support that point of view. Try it as an experiment. Try thinking from the opposite point of view about a particular subject and look for the evidence to support it. For instance, if there is someone in your life who is giving you problems, try thinking about them in opposite terms to how you have previously perceived them and look for evidence to support the new view.

To give a personal example: recently my car broke down and needed such costly repairs that it was not worth reviving. I was, therefore, temporarily car-less, which was, of course, annoying, inconvenient and all the rest. Rather than dwelling on the negative, though, the Pollyanna approach helped me recognise the benefits of having to walk (providing more exercise and opportunities to 'bump into' friends casually) and of travelling on public transport (thereby being more in contact with people and seeing posters advertising events I would not normally have known about). Focusing on the benefits empowered me.

Why do we think the way we do?

Many different schools of psychology have attempted to explain our mental processes and what determines our behaviour and reactions to the outside world. They have all made specific contributions to our understanding of ourselves, although this understanding is still incomplete.

One psychiatrist who made a major contribution to the subject, Dr Alfred Adler, maintained that we have formed a distinct view of the world by the time we are approximately five years old. This picture is created by everything that has surrounded and influenced us in those early years: the people, attitudes, atmosphere and feelings (of happiness, laughter, fear or sadness) and the rules and traditions (the 'do's' and the 'don'ts'). This picture becomes the 'norm' by which we measure the rest of our lives. If our life situation is similar to the early picture we have created, then we feel comfortable; but if it is dissimilar, we feel discomfort, and subconsciously set about recreating the old, familiar pattern. It may not be a pleasant pattern – very often the early picture we received of the world was far from ideal, perhaps it was unhappy or even frightening – but that becomes our 'norm', and we are only truly comfortable when we find ourselves (or put ourselves) in a similar scenario.

This hypothesis may explain why we often feel in a state of unease or conflict with life. There may be certain aspects of our lives or circumstances that we consciously dislike, but somehow we feel unable to do anything to change them. Therefore, in order to understand a little more clearly why you think and feel the way you do, and why your personal, working, financial or spiritual life is the way it is, you need to think back to the first five years of your childhood.

Ask yourself the following questions, to help clarify your current life situation. Write down the questions, and take as long as you need to write down the answers.

- What do you find most maddening or irritating about your current partner or a recent important partner?
- Where in your family were you born, i.e. were you the first born, the middle child of three, the youngest child, or an only child?

- What is your earliest memory?
- How did you feel at the time of this memory?
- Recall two other early memories. What were your feelings at the time of these memories?

Use an extra sheet of paper, or record your memories onto a tape recorder or Dictaphone. Then try to remember your feelings at these times and record them. Take as much time as you need, don't rush it; this is an investment in you.

Are some of the feelings you had in those early situations similar to the feelings you have today in difficult or stressful situations? Make a note of the emotions you feel currently and any similar emotions in the answers you have given.

Finding vulnerable areas

The first question relates to your early life conditioning. Dr Adler says, 'Tell me what you find most maddening or irritating about your spouse, partner or "significant other", and I will tell you why you are with them.' You are with them because of – not in spite of – the thing in them that is the most trouble to deal with. This difficulty is what you need in order to feel comfortable; it is what you experienced in your early childhood and has become an unconscious need. The important thing to realise is that you unconsciously chose that particular difficulty. It is not your partner's 'fault' that he or she has a particular personality. It is, rather, that you sought that personality trait because of some need or imbalance in yourself.

Looking at your life situation from this point of view may enable you to see it somewhat differently from the way you usually view it. This perspective may help you to understand in a new way the dynamics of some of your important relationships – and also how to arrive at the place you are aiming for, whether it is in your working or personal life.

You also have to spend a little time working out what it is that causes you always, or often, to end up somewhere else! When we achieve our goals, we become stress-free and are in harmony with ourselves; but if we set goals and objectives which we constantly fail to achieve, we will be in a state of inner turmoil and conflict. The reason we often fail to achieve what we say we want is because our conscious and subconscious minds are in conflict: they have different agendas.

The subconscious mind has been programmed long ago with a certain set of beliefs and norms, and the conscious mind is totally unaware of these. The conscious mind then sets a completely different agenda based on where you are right now and what you think would be desirable for the future. But, if what you want is at odds with the subconscious picture you have already installed as the 'norm', then there is a conflict: one level of consciousness is striving to make a particular scenario come true, while another level needs a different result; and so unease and stress ensue.

Now consider the other four questions listed above and the answers you gave. These should shed some light on your inner programming and what you subconsciously expect or need to prove as the truth. Take as long as you possibly can to write down or record – as vividly as possible – those early memories and the feelings you experienced.

Whichever early memory comes into your mind is the right one; just accept the first memory your subconscious mind produces – there will be a reason for it, which may or may not become clear. Become aware of the feelings you had, and try to get a sense of the atmosphere surrounding you at that time. Paint the picture fully in your imagination.

When you have the pictures anchored down by your written or spoken words, consider how they relate to your life today. Are there similarities with the current life patterns and situations that are causing you the most stress?

Whatever your current difficulties, try to relate them to the picture you have of your first five years or so. Then add to the list of feelings about your early life another list of these current problems, difficulties or stresses. Try to write alongside them how the two correspond. For example:

- Do you feel you are always in the wrong or do you find it difficult to express your opinions assertively? If so, who in your early life put you down or did not validate your opinions?
- Do you feel no one listens to you? Who in the first years didn't listen? Who do you want to listen to you?

- Do you feel angry much of the time? Who were you angry with in the first five years of your life?
- Do you feel dismissed, patronised, looked down on or slighted? Who made you feel this way as a child?
- Do you feel disappointed or let down by others most of the time? Think about how you were disappointed or let down by the most important people in your life when you were small; or about one particular incident that affected you deeply.
- Do you feel that you never get the recognition you deserve? Who did not give recognition to your endeavours when you were young? Who did not acknowledge your abilities sufficiently?

The questions listed above relate to our vulnerable spots, and when things start to go wrong for us, or feel especially difficult, it is often because one of the vulnerable spots has been activated and all the old, buried hurts or feelings of injustice, humiliation, inadequacy or fear attach themselves to the current situation, like iron filings to a magnet. The situation then feels somehow more extreme than it should, perhaps even overwhelming.

Sometimes, however, things can feel wrong or difficult because our current situation is so completely dissimilar to the early scenario that we feel like a 'fish out of water', or a 'bird in a cage': out of our true element and therefore uncomfortable. Here are some more examples to help you chart your vulnerable areas:

- If you were the youngest in the family and felt small and inadequate, is that a recurring theme in your life? Do you often feel inferior to others? Do you feel 'they' know more than you, or that somehow everyone around you seems older and more grown-up? Do you often feel that others are 'bigger' than you?
- Perhaps you were the youngest, but spoilt and 'babied' by your siblings: do you now yearn for that treatment from others? Do you expect special treatment? Do you perhaps feel put out or hard done by if others do not make you the centre of their attention? Do you feel you never get enough attention, whether generally,

from the important relationship in your life or from work colleagues?

- Were you the eldest child, looked up to by siblings, admired and accepted as the 'leader'? Were you always able to have your own way, without question, with brothers or sisters 'falling in' as rank and file followers? Do you now find it exceedingly irksome when others question your decisions or ideas, or when they do not automatically 'go along' with you? Do you resent anyone who has more power than you, or who does not automatically defer to your authority?

- Perhaps you had an idyllic early childhood. There was a sense of security, a happy and harmonious atmosphere; you may have had a beautiful garden to play in and the peace and clean air of the countryside. Nowadays you may always be trying to make relationships perfect and to create ideal situations instead of just going along with whatever happens. You find ordinary, everyday life difficult to come to terms with as you try to recreate an innocent, perfect Garden of Eden. Your world was perfect once upon a time, and subconsciously you will always be disappointed that no one can see that inner world. Until, that is, you meet someone who had a similar early life situation – you will then feel 'at home' with that partner.

A recent client had a recurring theme of not being able to make a commitment: she was always creating problems for the men in her relationships by going off with others. She couldn't understand why she seemed to need to be disruptive.

Early in her life, her parents had separated amicably, but she had been unable to accept her mother's new partner and became difficult and disruptive. After a number of therapy sessions, she realised that she had always created difficulties for others and had been seen as a problem. This was her 'norm', and she felt compelled to continue that pattern in her adult life – fulfilling an unconscious need to become a problem to the people closest to her, thereby confirming her internal picture of herself. Once she began to realise where these compulsions came from, she was able to give up the need for them and to settle down happily with her current boyfriend.

You will need to spend considerable time in looking at your vulnerable areas. You are bringing things from the unconscious to the surface; and it is only when they are conscious that you can deal with them. You can only change beliefs and attitudes when you are aware of having them. You cannot fight an unseen enemy.

Where do I go from here?

Once you understand a little more about why you see things the way you do, you can 'spring clean' those attitudes that are causing you the most trouble. Do some of them sound similar to those in the list below?

- 'I can never be the clever one.'
- 'I am not attractive, or capable, or artistic.'
- 'I can never win approval.'
- 'I can never win.'
- 'People are always trying to take advantage of me or cheat me.'
- 'Nobody listens to me.'
- 'Nobody appreciates how hard I work.'
- 'Nobody values my advice.'

At one time these thoughts may have been valid, but they need to be re-evaluated in relation to your life now, because a lot of what goes on in our lives is often in a time warp: we are living in the picture of the first five years of our life. We distort the present by projecting that early picture onto our current situations and relationships.

It's time to wake up to today. Today is not the first day of the rest of your life. Today is the only day of your life! It is the only time you have: this *now* moment is the only one in which you can achieve what you want. You cannot change the past and you cannot perform in the future. However, what you do now can affect the future, for better or worse, and can move you nearer to how you want it to be – once you stop reacting to a scenario that no longer exists.

You can choose to become free of the old 'scripts' that are running your life. Say to yourself out loud: 'I can be free to choose how I think.' Just because your internal computer has been programmed in a particular way, does not mean that you cannot change the programme.

But first of all you have to see clearly what you have been doing, and why. So often when things are not going too well we blame outside factors: other people, the government, the weather, our partners, what we ate for dinner last night. But in fact it is really what goes on inside our heads that dictates what – and where – we are.

As so much of our programming is subconscious, to reprogram our minds we have to work in a specific way on the subconscious part. Our subconscious mind believes everything that it is told: it does not discriminate or judge the material that it is fed. So, if you tell yourself you are no good at something – for example, that you are useless with money – then your subconscious mind will make sure that you function in such a way as to make that statement come true. If you tell yourself, or others, that you are sexually unattractive and undesirable, then that message gets fed in to the subconscious mind as a fact. Should a situation arise where you are beginning to get feedback that you are attractive or desirable, your subconscious will make sure that you sabotage the situation in order to confirm the original belief.

This process is very subtle: we do not consciously sabotage our chances for success, whether with potential partners, with finances, with our bosses or with important clients, but if we, or others, feed messages of failure into our subconscious mind, then that is what will manifest in our lives.

Choose to be free of the old programming

In order to achieve the world we want, we have to reprogram ourselves – wipe that internal tape clean and record new messages over the old ones. This means taking responsibility for what you think, making a pledge today to set about creating what you want.

Positive affirmations

One way to do this is with positive affirmations – remember that you already practise negative affirmations, or negative self-talk, much of the time. Simply turn the negative messages into positive ones and watch to see whether the subconscious will believe them – and therefore manifest this self-belief in our lives through real success.

You can begin by creating three positive statements each week, which you must say to yourself, over and over, many times a day – especially before you go to sleep, because then they will be more easily absorbed by your subconscious mind. Also, try to say them immediately on waking in the morning.

It is a good idea to write down these positive statements and pin them up some place that you look at frequently; or to carry them with you to refer to throughout the day.

The best way to begin creating your positive affirmations is to catch yourself saying something negative – either to someone else or to yourself – and turn that statement around, and say the opposite. For example:

- ✗ Negative statement: 'I never have enough time!'
- ✔ Positive statement: 'I always have enough time to achieve joyfully the things I need to achieve.'
- ✗ Negative statement: 'Things are out of control.'
- ✔ Positive statement: 'I happily control everything that I choose to control.'
- ✗ Negative statement: 'Nobody listens to me.'
- ✔ Positive statement: 'I feel peaceful that people listen to me as I wish to be listened to.'
- ✗ Negative statement: 'I can never influence people.'
- ✔ Positive statement: 'I am strong and convincing, and I feel confident of my ability to influence calmly anyone I choose.'

Positive affirmations should be made in the present tense, not the future tense, because the subconscious mind cannot know when in the future the statements will be true. It has to believe them *now*. The subconscious also needs clear statements which contain positive emotions, to humanise them.

Just write down all the negative thoughts that come into your mind regularly, and then work on turning them around into positive affirmations. We all need affirmation, but often we look to other people to give it to us; however, even when we are affirmed by someone else, frequently we don't accept it. So start now by taking in the positive from yourself. Don't wait for others to affirm you: affirm yourself.

Another way to affirm the positive

Make a list of what makes you feel stressed and unhappy in your life. Then make another list of what makes you feel happy and satisfied. Now, tear up the first list and keep the second list so that you can keep reading it, out loud if possible, many times each day. At the end of each week add at least one extra item to the list.

If there is a voice telling you that nothing makes you happy and satisfied, do *not* believe it! It is out of date. Look again.

The old adage 'count your blessings' is extremely wise. *What we give our attention to, we give our power.* So, give your attention to the positive, the list of blessings, and add to it regularly. And feel your positive power growing stronger.

Strengthening the positive

Every time you have a negative or critical thought, think the exact opposite and say it over and over in your mind. Don't comment on the positive, just say it. Even if a little voice (or a big voice) keeps telling you that this is ridiculous, or just plain untrue, keep on saying the opposite and accentuating the positive. You are calling up a picture of the opposite pole, creating balance.

Life is not all dark or all light; it is dark *and* light. Keep sight of the other side of the picture, which is also true. The negative voice or the critical voice may have some truth in it, but it is not the whole truth, and what we need to aim for is the whole picture: wholesomeness. We have to train ourselves to look for the positive, the good, the beautiful, then our inner world will be a better place in which to live, and our outer world will reflect this fact. We have a choice; we should exercise it.

The principle behind this thinking has been particularly well stated by the psychiatrist Roberto Assagioli:

The group of characteristics made up of appreciation, praise, gratitude and a constant emphasis on the good qualities of things, people and circumstances is usually referred to as optimism. But it is not a blind, superficial optimism. It is possible to see quite clearly all aspects of life, including the darker, negative ones, but then to consciously direct one's attention, interest and appreciation towards the positive aspects. This benevolent appreciation of the goodness and light in every thing and every being makes life easier and more joyful.[1]

Trapped in the Stress Response

If you are finding it hard to be positive it may well be that you are caught in the Stress Response, in which everything is geared up to save your life: your perspective inevitably narrows down and you block out everything that is unnecessary for helping you to get out of danger. In a real 'life or death' situation, of course, this is what is required; but in less extreme circumstances, the result is that we block out many ideas that could help us. To repeat: under stress we constrict, become narrow-minded, blinkered, tunnel-visioned.

Try to be aware of when this is happening to you and take steps to keep your mind as broad as possible by widening your perspective. Take responsibility for nourishing and nurturing your mind, even when it feels a little difficult.

Balancing left and right brain

Try to balance left-brain and right-brain activity regularly, using some of the suggestions discussed earlier and thinking up some more for yourself. For example, if you have been using the left, logical, verbal side of the brain for some hours, then switch to the right, creative side by walking around, singing – yes, even in the middle of the day – or drawing a few funny pictures, or just looking out of the window for a few moments. Here are some more suggestions:

Read positive, uplifting, or educational books.
There are so many helpful books available now; just go into your local bookstore and browse around. You may be surprised by what you find and what you are drawn towards – perhaps inspirational literature or poetry. You may never

[1] From Roberto Assagioli, MD, *Transpersonal Development: The Dimension Beyond Psychosynthesis,* The Aquarian Press, an imprint of HarperCollins, 1991.

have thought of reading poetry, but if you give it a try and put any prejudices about 'not being able to understand it' to one side, you may find it enjoyable, even uplifting.

If you buy books, mark the passages that are important and meaningful, and turn to them as an instant support system to lift your mood or widen your perspective. If you cannot afford to buy books, copy out these passages.

Read biographies of people you admire.
These can be extremely inspirational and encouraging, for they usually confirm that people who have achieved something and whom we respect have not had trouble-free lives! Biographies can give us the courage to keep on struggling with our difficulties, and we can gain new perspectives.

Listen to beautiful, happy and optimistic music.
When listening to music or looking at pictures, we use the right hemisphere of the brain, which is refreshing and restful, as most of the time we are functioning out of the left hemisphere, which is the sphere of words and logic. So, a regular switch to the right side of the brain is balancing and restorative. Have uplifting music playing in the background when you are carrying out repetitive or boring chores, or when you are driving.

Look at uplifting, beautiful objects and paintings.
Visit art galleries, stately homes or museums (where you may also find well-designed furniture and wonderful architecture). This feeds the senses and rests the mind by allowing it to focus on things other than the usual daily preoccupations.

Watch videos or go to the cinema.
As pictures also shift us into the right hemisphere of the brain, films can broaden our perspective, so long as the subject matter is not depressing or violent. Nature and travel films can be wonderful sources of new and beautiful images that will refresh and restore the tired, strained and overworked left hemisphere.

See the funny side of things.
Try to look for this dimension when things are getting you down. Laughter is one of life's greatest therapies; it certainly

puts things in perspective and cuts problems down to size. A wonderful book on the subject of laughter, as being vital to the healing process and the successful outcome of illness, is *Anatomy of an Illness* by Norman Cousins. See Suggested Further Reading.

Wander through parks and gardens.

This, again, will give the mind refreshment and time to dream. It is very important to have time to daydream. Often the solutions we have been striving for suddenly present themselves when we stop focusing and forcing the mind.

Constantly refresh your mind by taking in all kinds of new stimuli: new ideas, new sights and new sounds. Think of your own ways to fill your mind with beauty, light and quality impressions.

> *We become that which we behold* – William Blake

As stated earlier, the subconscious mind believes what it is told, so limit the negative impressions you allow into your mind. Don't watch too much bad news on TV or too many violent or depressing programmes; the same principle applies to what you read. In fact, many people, when they are in the Stress Response, find that they actually cannot bear to watch television or read the newspapers; their minds are already in overload and they have no spare capacity for coping with any more negative images or problematic situations. They have reached their limits of adaptation to outside circumstances and they need time to replenish their reserves. Most importantly, they need to sleep as much as they can to restore the mind.

Again, Shakespeare illustrates the point most beautifully:

Sleep that knits up the ravell'd sleave of care,
The death of each day's life, sore labour's bath,
Balm of hurt minds, great nature's second course
Chief nourisher in life's feast.

Macbeth (Act 2: Scene ii)

Do not take difficult people to bed with you!

Try to leave the problems of the day and thoughts of difficult and unappealing people outside the bedroom door at night. Visualise yourself removing all the burdens, problems and difficult people from wherever you feel you carry them, and putting them somewhere permanent for the night. Then you can go into your bedroom free of encumbrances and able to enjoy peaceful sleep. In the morning you can pick up all of these burdens again, if you want to take them into the next day, or you could just leave them be and start afresh.

Create positive visualisations and images in your mind
If you are unable to travel, or get out and about much, this does not mean you should be resigned to thinking negative thoughts. If you begin to feel down or depressed, think something cheerful, uplifting or optimistic. Refuse to accept depressing thoughts or images and refuse to allow your mind to think about problems, failures or fears. Just say 'No!' to your mind – you are 'The Boss'.

Instead, think about peaceful situations, or imagine a scene or an object that is calming or reassuring. Call these things into your mind when you are troubled or anxious. For example, imagine you are lying on a beautiful beach, fringed with palm trees, in the sun, feeling peaceful and at rest. Or picture your favourite flower, tree or precious stone; let the image calm and uplift you.

If your mind keeps trying to go back to the worrying or depressing thoughts, just firmly and gently bring it back to the picture you want to focus on. The more you practise this technique, the better you will become at taking control and deciding what you want in your mind rather than accepting whatever your mind decides to dump on you.

Create a 'Belief Statement'

Write out a statement to yourself outlining your beliefs and the rules and values you live by. It could be written as a series of sentences:

● I believe the only way to be happy is to make someone else happy every day of my life.

- I believe in working hard and playing hard.
- I believe in the power of love.
- As you sow, so shall you reap.
- Nothing comes for nothing.
- *Honi soit qui mal y pense.* (Evil be to him who evil thinks.)
- You can tell a lot about a person by his/her friends.
- By their fruits ye shall know them.
- Never do today what you can do tomorrow, and if you put it off long enough you may never have to do it.
- Never put off until tomorrow what you can do today.
- Emphasise the positive.
- *Noblesse oblige.*
- There are no free dinners.
- There are occasional free lunches!
- If you always do what you have to do, you never do what you want to do.

Put this 'Belief Statement' where you will see it often, and read it frequently. Update it from time to time as something new and important occurs to you. Work with it in a dynamic way, rewrite it in a different form. Be creative: write different beliefs in different colours, or turn it into a diagram or a drawing. Your 'Statement' is about how you live your life.

Think positive, think happy, think beautiful, think true, think kind, think generous, think harmony, think co-operation, think peace, think love. Think anything you want to think!

Chapter Six

You are What You Eat and Drink

It is important to support yourself with good nutrition at all times, but it is particularly important when you are feeling stressed, strained or overloaded. At times of stress there is often an urge to turn to food and drink as a sort of 'comforter', in an unconscious wish to return to a previous stage when we were not required to handle too much responsibility.

We feel cared for and momentarily secure when we pop a little 'goody' into our mouths, especially, it seems, if that goody contains sugar or fat. This reaction when under duress is entirely understandable in terms of comforting ourselves, but it is harmful to the body to indulge too often in sugary or fat-drenched, salty snacks, or in too much junk or fast food, not to mention overdosing on caffeine and alcohol.

Low-quality food creates a huge problem for the body when it comes to maintaining its organs and systems, because it provides insufficient quantities of the correct substances. It also causes a lot of toxic waste, which makes us feel run down and low in energy; and so we reach for a 'treat' to lift us up, in the form of sweets, crisps, sweet drinks, caffeine and alcohol. These 'rewards' for dealing with the strain of life will not harm us too much if we only indulge in them occasionally, but they do not provide the body with what it needs to produce abundant health and vitality from day to day.

Eat less:

Sugar

In the Stress Response, your body releases extra sugar (see page 28), so it needs less by mouth. Sugar provides empty calories; it gives you energy for physical exertion, but no essential raw materials for replenishing the cells of the body. You may get an immediate 'high' from sugary foods or drinks, but this wears off very quickly and is followed by a sudden drop in energy and a 'low' feeling. High sugar intake literally starves you. It also puts a strain on the pancreas which can lead to malfunction. By reducing sugar you also reduce the risk of coronary heart disease. Check for hidden sugar in foods such as cereals, tinned fruit and vegetables, bread, sauces, etc. Eat natural sugar found in fresh and dried fruit, raisins, dates, blackstrap molasses and pure honey, or buy pure fructose (fruit sugar) from health food stores.

Fat

Fat should not be cut out altogether: it is necessary for the absorption of the fat-soluble vitamins A, D, E and K, for maintaining healthy cell membranes and for building a strong immune system. It is only harmful when eaten to excess, and should make up no more than 30 per cent of total daily intake, of which only 10 per cent should be saturated fat (animal fat). Use olive oil instead of butter or lard, especially for cooking, as it does not oxidise when heated, which other vegetable oils do, producing harmful free radicals.

All oils should be refrigerated to prevent them turning rancid. While olive oil has beneficial properties for health, it is also very fattening, so consume in moderation. Fats contain approximately twice as many calories as carbohydrates and proteins, and saturated fats are especially harmful when you are in the Stress Response, due to the body's production of extra cholesterol and free fatty acids to aid you in Fight or Flight. Grill or bake foods rather than frying in fat, and remember the 'hidden' fats in food like pork, breast of lamb, sausages, bacon, egg yolks, gravy, cheese, puddings, biscuits and pastries.

Salt

The average person needs approximately one-third of a tea-spoon of salt (sodium) per day. Strenuous exercise and excessive sweating in hot weather could increase your salt needs due to high amounts being lost in your sweat, but most people consume far more salt than is necessary for the body's healthy function. Excessive sodium can damage your kidneys and cause high blood pressure, strokes and heart failure. Fluid retention due to potassium loss can also result from a diet high in salt, contributing to pre-menstrual tension and causing serious problems during pregnancy. Avoid too many salty snacks, like salted nuts and crisps, and savory or cheese biscuits. Hard cheeses have a high salt content, as do tinned and processed foods, especially processed meats. Try not to add extra salt to food on your plate and use small amounts in cooking; enhance flavours with herbs, lemon juice or spices. If a low-salt diet is unpalatable for you, try using potassium chloride, which is stocked at most health food stores instead of sodium chloride (kitchen salt). But best of all is to train your taste buds not to need too much salt.

Eat more:

Fresh vegetables

Preferably eat vegetables raw – most vegetables taste delicious in their uncooked state. When cooking, steam or use very little water to avoid losing too many vitamins. If fresh vegetables are not available, the best alternative is frozen, as their vitality is preserved up to a point by the freezing process. Whenever possible, choose organically grown produce to avoid the toxins of chemical pesticides and fertilisers, which overload the body with toxic waste and require valuable energy to eliminate.

Salad foods

All the foods normally associated with salads, such as lettuce, cucumber, tomatoes, mushrooms, peppers, celery, celeriac (celery root), radishes, avocados, endive, fennel, watercress, parsley, etc., are brimming with vitamins and minerals (as are all raw vegetables). Cooking destroys many of these nutrients. Equally important is that these foodstuffs have a high water content, which assists in their assimilation. It is more difficult for the body to digest and absorb concentrated foods, which should be eaten in smaller amounts.

Fresh fruit

This is another vital, high-water-content food (80–90 per cent water content). Fruit should always be eaten uncooked, as cooking turns it acidic, forcing the body to use precious energy to neutralise it; cooking also destroys most, if not all, of its health-giving nutrients. Fruit is considered to be the most beneficial food of all, supplying every nutrient needed for optimum health: glucose, amino acids, fatty acids, minerals and vitamins. Fruit should be eaten on an empty stomach, as it is digested very quickly, only remaining in the stomach for about thirty minutes before passing into the intestines. If you eat fruit at the end of a meal, it gets held up in the stomach behind the other food and begins to ferment, losing its goodness and often causing flatulence. So eat it first thing in the morning: it will supply you with plenty of energy to face the day and assist in the body's elimination processes. When you crave a snack between meals, eat fruit or raw vegetables.

Fibre

Fibre is one of the most essential components of a healthy diet, especially when you are stressed. Fibre assists the efficient elimination of toxins and waste, one of the main keys to maintaining good health. It is difficult for the body to remain healthy if poisons are circulating and waste material is being stored rather than excreted. Fibre acts like a sponge or blotting paper in your body by absorbing undigested food and excess cholesterol, including the cholesterol produced internally as a response to stress. Foods containing fibre, or roughage, are: fresh fruit, vegetables (especially raw vegetables), whole grains like brown rice, oats (particularly effective at soaking up cholesterol), wheat germ, millet, rye, barley, maize, muesli (check for added sugar), wholewheat pasta, wholemeal bread and crispbreads, high-fibre biscuits, oatcakes, high-fibre cereals like All Bran, baked potatoes, baked beans, seeds, sweetcorn, unsalted nuts, pulses like lentils, peas, mung beans, kidney beans and aduki beans. Sufficient fibre will be obtained from a mixed diet of the above foods.

Good and Poor Choices in a Stress-Buffering Diet

BREAKFAST

GOOD CHOICES

- ✔ Fresh mixed-fruit salad
- ✔ Grapefruit/melon
- ✔ Muesli or high-fibre cereal, with skimmed milk, fruit sugar (fructose)
- ✔ Wholewheat toast or crisp bread with honey, sugar-free jam, or low-salt, savoury spread
- ✔ Boiled/scrambled egg (no more 3 or 4 times per week)
- ✔ Fruit juice, tea/herb tea, decaffeinated coffee or dandelion coffee

POOR CHOICES

- ✘ No breakfast
- ✘ Tinned fruit/sugary syrup
- ✘ Low-fibre, sugar-enriched cereal
- ✘ Fried foods such as egg, bacon, sausages, fried bread, etc.
- ✘ White, refined-flour bread with high-sugar jam/syrup
- ✘ Sugary biscuits
- ✘ Strong coffee/lots of sugar
- ✘ Sweets/chocolate bars/crisps

LUNCH

GOOD CHOICES

- ✔ Melon/fresh fruit cocktail
- ✔ Huge salad with as many raw vegetables as possible and/or cooked fresh vegetables
- ✔ Jacket potato (eat skin)
- ✔ Rice (preferably brown)
- ✔ Small amount of protein (meat 2–4 times per week; fish 2–3 times per week)
- ✔ Cauliflower cheese
- ✔ Small vegetable pasta dish
- ✔ Soup/wholemeal bread/salad
- ✔ Baked beans/scrambled egg
- ✔ Omelette or vegeburger
- ✔ Mineral water/fruit juice
- ✔ 1 glass wine/ 1/2 pint beer

POOR CHOICES

- ✘ Fried potatoes (have occasionally as a treat)
- ✘ Fried fish, sausages, hamburgers (grill them instead)
- ✘ No salads/raw or fresh vegetables
- ✘ Tinned vegetables too often
- ✘ Rich, creamy sauces (hard to digest, will make you sleepy)
- ✘ Huge pasta dish (have a small portion with salad and/or vegetables)
- ✘ Rich, creamy dessert
- ✘ Sausage, egg and chips
- ✘ Sugary soft drinks
- ✘ More than 1 unit of alcohol

DINNER

GOOD CHOICES	POOR CHOICES
✔ Melon/avocado/grapefruit	✘ Processed/high-salt meats
✔ Prawn/seafood cocktail	✘ Smoked fish/meat too often
✔ Soup (homemade, if possible)	✘ Fatty meats – pork, lamb,
✔ Grilled/roast meat	chicken skin, fatty mince
✔ Baked/grilled fish	hamburgers, sausages – more
✔ Casserole of meat or fish or	than once per week
vegetables	✘ High-cholesterol-forming
✔ Vegetables au gratin	dishes/sauces with high
✔ Pulses/rice	butter/cream content
✔ Lots of fresh vegetables	✘ High sugar/cream content
✔ Pasta or curry (meat/veg-	desserts like: ice cream,
etable)	sorbets, trifles, gateaux, etc.
✔ Low-fat yoghurt/ice cream	✘ Tinned fruit
✔ Herb/camomile tea	✘ Sugary soft drinks
✔ Milky drink at bedtime	✘ Strong coffee

The 'Poor Choice' foods can be consumed occasionally without weakening your stress defences too seriously, but they
should not form the largest part of your diet. Try to choose
most of your foods from the 'Good Choices' selection, and
you will boost your defences against stress and illness.

Vitamins and mineral supplements

If you are eating a properly balanced diet, your body should
be well buffered against the demands of everyday stresses.
However, if your stress levels increase due to excessive sleep
loss, chronic fatigue, illness, emotional upset, overcrowding,
lack of control, noise pollution or too much change, the extra
demand on your adaptive capacities causes every nutrient to
be needed in larger-than-usual amounts. Therefore, at those
times when the demands on you are extreme, you should take
a daily multi-vitamin and mineral supplement, as well as
extra vitamin C (up to 1000 mg) per day. The need for vitamin C is increased tremendously by stress, as is the need for
pantothenic acid, which can be taken in tablet form or by eating lots of green leafy vegetables, eggs, wheat bran and
peanuts (preferably unsalted). Smoking (a terrible stress for

the body) also increases your vitamin C requirement. Zinc tends to be depleted at times of stress, although beware of taking excess zinc, as this can cause copper deficiency and lead to anaemia. Zinc is found in eggs, meat, seafood (especially oysters). If you are under a lot of emotional or mental stress, I would suggest a supplement of the B-complex vitamins, but do not exceed the recommended daily allowance. Supplements should be seen as just that, to be taken alongside a healthy diet, not as substitutes for good food.

Water

It is desirable to drink about eight glasses, or at least two litres, of water in each 24-hour day. Make sure that you drink at least half a pint before retiring to bed, and another half-pint on rising in the morning. Have some bottled water in your bedroom so that you can also drink some if you should wake in the middle of the night. Distilled water is actually the best, although it can be rather tasteless.

When flying it is particularly important to drink plenty of water, as the air pressure inside the plane dehydrates you. You will feel less jet-lag at the end of your journey if you drink at least a pint of water per flying hour, and try not to consume alcohol or coffee, as both dehydrate the body.

Drinking plenty of water also thins the blood (especially desirable when in the Stress Response, which causes the production of extra blood-thickening factors). It also ensures frequent urine excretion and dilutes concentrates of toxins in the bladder, thereby reducing the possibility of bladder infection. Another positive by-product will be a clearer and more youthful skin condition, as the skin becomes more wrinkled when we don't consume enough water.

Alleviating panic attacks and PMS

The latest thinking about diet and nutrition is that we should eat little and often. We are said to be grazing animals, and so eating as animals do in a pasture – a small amount with small gaps in between – is the easiest way for the body to cope with the food we ingest, and is the least likely way to put on weight. When we go for long periods without eating, the body thinks it risks starvation, and so takes in more at the next opportunity to stock up, just in case. Also, if we go without food for many hours our blood sugar level drops, and this is thought to contribute to panic attacks. When the blood sugar drops below a certain level, the body releases adrenaline to keep us going, and it is this excess of adrenaline that can cause shakiness and the symptoms of panic attacks. So, if you suffer from panic attacks, make sure that you eat something, preferably of a starchy nature, every three to four hours. Eating something at frequent intervals also helps with premenstrual syndrome, reducing the symptoms of weepiness, aggressiveness and general mood swings.

So what needs changing?

All this talk of what is the best way to eat may leave you feeling a little bewildered about where, if anywhere, to start to change your eating habits. The best way to begin to address this question is to work out exactly what you are already eating. I suggest that for a week, or even better for a fortnight, you write down everything you have eaten and drunk that day. You may not like what you see, but once you have realised what you are actually eating, it should not be too difficult to work out where adjustments need to be made – what you need more of and what you need to cut down on – following the guidelines in this chapter.

Try not to eat when you are feeling very stressed and wound up, emotionally upset or angry, because you will not be able to digest your food properly. In the Stress Response, the digestive system partially or completely shuts down (see page 30), and so eating in this condition may cause you violent indigestion, and will certainly mean that you do not receive the full goodness from your food. Before eating, try to have a few moments of stillness, to calm down and relax.

Chapter Seven

Somebody Loves Me – Managing Relationships

Research studies show that people who have close relationships or good personal support systems succumb less to stress and stress-related illnesses than those who feel isolated and unsupported. Whether we feel lonely or supported does not necessarily depend on how many people we have in our lives; it depends mostly on the *quality* of our relationships.

When you are extremely busy, you may feel you have no time for other people, and, of course, we all need time alone to recharge our energies; but prioritising a percentage of your time for your relationships and for creating supportive networks of people around you is sensible life-management, as well as being a wise investment in your future. In today's changing world, many of the things you rely on for your sense of identity and wellbeing could suddenly be lost – your job, home, standard of living and so on – but supportive relationships can be the calm place in the midst of the storm.

One recent research study of 2,300 men with heart disease showed that those with a highly stressful lifestyle and few friends were six times more likely to die than those with less-stressful lives and many friends.[1] Many similar studies have found that friends and supportive relationships were important contributing factors in recovery from illness.

Research also indicates that men under pressure tend to contract, withdraw, become uncommunicative and bottle things up; whereas women under pressure are more likely to expand, taking on more and more, sublimating their stress into displacement activities and exhausting themselves in the process. Both kinds of responses are extreme and add to the problem of pressure rather than solving it. Try to recognise

[1] This statistic is taken from David Lewis and John Storey, MD: *The Doctor's Heart Attack Recovery Plan*, Thorsons, London, 1990.

when you have gone into either mode and try to develop the humility and wisdom to acknowledge that you may not be reacting in the best possible way.

This is where friends and relations can be helpful, as they may be able to see more clearly what is happening to you and persuade you to take it a bit easier and stop exhausting yourself or to open up and talk about the stress you are experiencing. So, when you feel that things are on top of you, turn to other people to help you cope; see your relationships as resources on which to draw in times of crisis and difficulty; do not try to stand alone and be independent.

Often, when people feel particularly stressed, they tend to cut themselves off from relationships, feeling unable to give very much of themselves to the various people in their life. This becomes a vicious circle, in that, the more you cut yourself off, the more you feel isolated and deprived and so have even less to give. But you also cut yourself off from what others could give to you; in fact, asking for support can make the people in your life feel valuable and useful, and it means they can draw on you in turn when they feel troubled.

However, in order to draw upon relationships when you need them, you must nurture and develop them along the way. You must invest in them some time, energy and creativity, so that they can give you in return all that they potentially contain when you most need it.

So pick up the telephone, make that call or write that letter. Make the effort even when you don't feel in the mood, and most likely it will lift your mood.

You might like to copy out the positive list opposite and add to it all the positive gifts you recognise receiving from your relationships. Pin it up where you will see it frequently and continue to add any extra points as they reveal themselves. Make sure you look at it whenever you are inclined to isolate yourself. Feel the warmth and energy coming towards you from those positive words.

What a difference a smile makes. The Dalai Lama says, 'I am quite sure that if this fourteenth Dalai Lama smiled less, perhaps I would have fewer friends in various places.' He maintains that, 'whether president, queen or beggar, there is no difference, provided that there is genuine human feeling with a genuine human smile of affection.'

GOOD RELATIONSHIPS GIVE	**BAD RELATIONSHIPS CAUSE**
✔ Joy	✘ Depression
✔ Fun	✘ Anxiety
✔ A sense of belonging	✘ Social isolation
✔ Confidence	✘ Erosion of confidence
✔ Increased resistance to stress	✘ Decreased resistance to stress
✔ Emotional security	✘ Emotional deprivation
✔ Encouragement	✘ Feelings of discouragement
✔ Feelings of self-worth	✘ Diminished self-esteem
✔ Stimulation	✘ Negative introspection
✔ A place for emotions	✘ Feelings of self-pity
✔ Recreation	✘ Loneliness
✔ Support	✘ Envy of others

Relationships need practice

Relating to other people is, of course, not always easy, as we are constantly bumping up against all the unseen, sensitive sides of them. Rather like icebergs, we all have dangerous, jagged parts hidden below the surface, and when you feel overloaded you may not relish taking on the work of a relationship. You may even agree with Jean-Paul Sartre that 'Hell is other people.' Also, if you have allowed yourself to become too isolated for too long, it is quite difficult to get back into the state of openness and willingness to tolerate the imperfections in others that is required for relating.

But our relationships are the spice and seasoning of our lives, without which life might be easier and less painful, but bland and dull, and we would learn less. We need feedback from others to help us develop and to keep us in touch with reality, as well as to support and help us through life.

Try to see all interaction between yourself and others as an opportunity to improve your interpersonal skills. This can be a helpful way to approach difficulties in relationships; don't expect to make them perfect overnight, just expect them to get better gradually. Sometimes you will fail, but keep on with the practice, and your performance is bound to improve.

- If you have been upset, angry or hurt, try to see the reactions from other people as merely useful information from which you can learn.
- Try to look at the feedback you have received without emotion, perhaps imagining that it was aimed at some one else, and attempt to extrapolate the lesson. This is not easy to do, but it gets easier with practise – and I am not saying that it is always you who must adjust.
- If you experience the same difficulties over and over again with someone, the lesson may be to avoid that person as much as possible in future. If you have done all you can to try to understand why the interaction between you is unsatisfactory and stressful, then it is pointless to continue to receive the stress.

In addition to the relationships you have with your partner, your family, your friends, work colleagues and neighbours, there are other relationships that can be complementary – for example:

- Casual, passing relationships: with the bus driver, the corner newsagent, a waiter/waitress in a restaurant or just a stranger who smiles in passing as your eyes meet on a busy street – these contacts can be extraordinarily uplifting and change your mood in an instant.
- Therapeutic relationships: with your doctor, dentist, hairdresser, counsellor, aromatherapist, osteopath, masseur, physiotherapist and therapists of all kinds.

These different relationships can balance each other, so if one is causing you stress, then you may be able to de-stress yourself by turning to one of the others. Absorb all the good you can from an uplifting interaction or an enhancing relationship so that you have renewed vigour and enthusiasm to go back and tackle the difficult ones.

Keeping the compartments separate

Think of your life in compartments and protect the boundary between one compartment and another, so that you can walk through into a stress-free space. Try not to bring the stresses from work into the home compartment, walking through the front door in an irritable or prickly mood, causing loved ones to feel resentful at being the dumping ground for the fallout from somewhere else, and so causing the place in which you should rest and recover from the stresses of the day to become another problem area.

The same applies if you allow problems with your home relationships to leak into the work compartment. You then create unnecessary difficulties in that area of your life, perhaps by being short-tempered with, or withdrawn from, colleagues or clients. Instead of taking your stresses into work, try to see your workplace as an area where you de-stress and get a better perspective on what is happening at home, so that you can return home refreshed by the support and stimulation of work colleagues.

The social compartment can often seem too much to cope with if you feel stressed and overloaded by the other two, but it may be the way out of problems by helping you to unwind and restore yourself.

Do not allow one life area to contaminate the others.

- Make a space between the compartments by literally stopping for a few moments to be still and relax, to breathe out and consciously let go of all the tensions you may be carrying. Do this before you go into work and especially before you return home after work or before entering a friend's house. Just stop wherever you are for five minutes and practise the relaxation skills set out in Chapter 3. Then you can enter the next compartment of your life freed up from the previous one, fresh for whatever comes next.
- If you drive between work and home, you can do this in your car. If you are not travelling by car, you can still let go, relax and breathe out on the train, in the bus or just stand still in the street – you can pretend to be looking in a shop window, or to be reading a poster

or notice board.

- You can do it at your desk, between meetings or between different pieces of work, and before you leave in the evening.
- Just closing your eyes for five minutes can give you space between one thing and another: close your eyes, breathe out and let go.

You will find this letting go and the creation of a space between compartments makes you feel lighter in body and spirit, as you release the tensions and become more alert to the moment.

Play in your relationships

If you are a stressed mother or father, just let go of the striving for a while and play with your children. Stop resisting their noise and energy and go with it. This is a great way to unwind and to give vent to the child that is still within you. Playing with children allows you to be silly and frivolous, which can be great for releasing tensions, especially if you are a parent who is out working all day.

The inner child is the child that we once were, the part of us that revels in play, that can be spontaneous, creative, full of life, enthusiasm and joy. It can also be the side of us that is petulant, moody and uncooperative, and may need a good talking to! But usually, when the negative traits of the child manifest themselves, it is because that aspect of you is not being given sufficient acknowledgement: if you allow it some time for expression, some outlet somewhere, you will feel freer and more energised as a result, and much less irritable.

Recreational moments in relationships release creative abilities and output, especially in the working environment where fun seems to be in short supply. Although one can't play games in the office, a moment of lightness allows everyone to relax and will enhance performance in the long run.

In relationships with partners, friends and family, it is so easy always to be engaged in serious matters that you forget to have fun together. Make sure you have sufficient recreational time for the obvious pursuits such as sport, visiting the countryside or the seaside, going to the theatre or to concerts, going out dancing or staying in with friends or watching videos at home – the list is endless. Have fun in all the many relationships in your life and constantly re-create yourself and others. Be in a state of joy as often as possible.

Relationships are essential for our emotional health, because they are the arena in which we can risk expressing the range of our emotions and in which the 'inner child' can be looked after as well as expressed. We all need love, and good relationships offer unlimited potential for giving and receiving it. But we have to allow ourselves to relax into relationships and work on them.

The necessity of this was eventually realised by a client who recognised that his marriage felt stale and boring because he and his wife had lost touch with the child side of themselves. They had got into a rut of only talking about arrangements and the children, and watching too much television. I suggested that they turn the television off for one evening each week, which they did and found that they enjoyed the time this released. They had an opportunity just to 'hang out' together, as he put it; and so they decided to cut back their viewing time even further. They began chatting more at the end of the day, became more light-hearted, started having dinner at the dining table instead of on their knees in front of the television, and their relationship revived. So often the fun element can go missing.

Some ideas for play and fun in relationships

- Put on some music that you both enjoy and dance together. You don't have to go out to night clubs to enjoy dancing; just do it at home, and see how enlivening it can be. Dancing is great exercise, so if you are not an exercise fan, dance instead, as it works the cardiovascular system just as well as aerobics. Alternatively, you could join a dance class together.
- Give each other some massage; it doesn't matter how 'expert' you are so long as you are gentle and ask for feedback from your partner about what feels good and which parts of his or her body need soothing. The important thing about this is just giving the time to touching each other in a pleasurable way. It will be

relaxing for both of you. Massaging children is also a great way to relax them for sleep.

- Instead of sitting at a table for supper, sometimes have a picnic on a rug or a blanket on the floor. This can make you feel as if you are on holiday; it can be great fun and very unwinding.
- While you are picnicking, or playing in any other way, put on the answering machine and resist all urges to answer the telephone, unless it is a matter of life or death. Machines are supposed to help us, not make life more stressful, so use them to provide 'time off'.
- Do lots of things by candlelight – eating, talking, listening to music, bathing – as this creates a romantic and relaxed atmosphere – a 'recreational' atmosphere. Of course, make love by candlelight.
- Make love in different places: on the carpet or on cushions in front of the fire, in the shower, in the bath, on the sofa, in the garden in the dark on a summer night, or wherever your imagination takes you.
- Read favourite childhood stories to each other.
- Sing together, especially when you are in the car. It brings your breathing down to your diaphragm and is very relaxing. Sing with children when you are driving them around; it channels their energy and can relieve car sickness because singing makes them breathe more deeply and take in more oxygen.
- Take a boat out on the river or the lake in the park.

These are just a few ideas to get your imagination started; I am sure you can think up many, many other ways to play.

Nurturing your relationships

'A trouble shared is a trouble halved' is a wise old saying. In close relationships you can experience yourself more fully than in a business one, but each sort of relationship has possibilities for providing an outlet for your various sides. So, by keeping your relationships healthy, you will be keeping your psychological self healthy and building resistance to stress.

A good friend always quotes her mother: 'To have good friends, you must be a good friend.' My friend obviously applied this admonition, as she has a huge circle of friends who have proved all-important in helping her through a recent separation and divorce. Her friends have been so valuable because they have given her love when she was feeling unlovable. When one person in your life stops loving you, it is easy to assume that no one will ever love you again; and in such circumstances we badly need the other relationships – to give the lie to that understandable assumption.

Relationships can be developed from a casual level to a deeper one – if you give them the time and commitment. Give time and love to the people in your life and it will return to you in equal measure. The more you give, the more you will receive – not necessarily from the same source, but in my experience when you give out, something always comes back to you from somewhere. Giving also makes you aware of what you have to offer and therefore helps you to see your own value more clearly. In order to nurture your relationships:

- Remember people's birthdays – send cards.
- Write or call to say 'thank you'.
- Call friends and leave special excerpts of music, poetry, items of mutual interest or even jokes on their answering machines.
- Arrange frequent get-togethers, which need not cost a great deal; suggest that everyone brings a contribution in terms of food and drink.
- Never pass up an opportunity to celebrate with the people you love.
- When you feel low or depressed, search out people who make you feel good about yourself – those who love and/or admire you, and who, above all, accept you and give you positive feedback about yourself.

When you feel stressed or strained, call up in your imagination all the people in your life who care for you now and who have cared for you in the past. Recognise, or reassess, the support systems that surround you. See Useful Addresses for counselling and support groups. Look at your most significant relationships and decide how you could improve them. Perhaps draw up a list of goals for your relationships: refer to it frequently, and keep working at it. Try to see every encounter with another person as an opportunity to practise your relationship skills. See every difficult encounter as useful feedback. Attempt to analyse what went wrong, and how you could have handled it differently. Visualise yourself interacting as you wish you had done, and play it over and over in your imagination. Remember:

- Good relationships create joy.
- Unsatisfactory relationships create stress.

Communication

Often the reason certain relationships are not satisfying is because we are not being honest in them, or we are playing some sort of game or role. You may be trying to be too nice – playing Mr Nice Guy or Ms Wonderful – to gain approval, to be liked or to protect yourself against confrontation. If you often feel inwardly hurt or angry with other people, this could be a sign that you are being too nice, too much of the time; that you are not being assertive enough to get your needs met or your side of things understood. The following exercise may help you to see what you are doing.

- Stand in front of a mirror and say out loud everything you would like to say to someone who is making you feel uncomfortable. Say it again and again, and when you have vented all the emotion, try to reword your message without any emotion – just the facts.
- State the facts over and over to yourself in the mirror, and when you have the facts clear, then say how you feel about those facts. This way you do not muddle up the facts with the emotions; and the message you give to the other person will some across more clearly.

Another role you may be playing is that of superiority, in which case you will not be able to allow your vulnerabilities and weaknesses to show, which could leave you feeling lonely and alienated from close relationships. In order to be close to someone you have to be willing to remove your 'mask'. If you insist on wearing the mask, of 'the invincible one', or 'the one who always knows best', then you must also be prepared to pay a price in terms of loneliness or a lack of close relationships. It is only when someone discloses their inner doubts and fears that others can begin to get close. If you always have a protective barrier up, people can't get close to you. A defensive, superior or aloof manner communicates a powerful 'keep your distance' message. Could it be that this is what you are inadvertently conveying in some of your relationships?

Obviously you cannot be informal and intimate with everybody; there are some relationships that require formality and distance, but it is worth giving some thought to the way you are relating to the significant people in your life. Is it the best way to get what you want and need from them?

Different kinds of communication

There are so many ways of communicating the same message, it can be interesting to practise a number of different styles and notice the different reactions you receive. It has been found, in various sociological studies, that the actual words we use are the least important part of any message. Many of these studies have reached a consensus that:

- Body language conveys 55 per cent of any message
- Tone of voice conveys 38 per cent of the message
- Words carry just 7 per cent of the total message

These findings can be used to explain why we are often attracted to people who are not necessarily on our mental wavelength – the non-verbal messages are so powerful. This also explains why telephonic and electronic relationships are unsatisfactory, because we are starved of so many of the signals we actually need for total communication. In our working relationships this can sometimes seem like an advantage, but in the long run face-to-face communication has more potential for success.

If you have trouble communicating, or if this is an area of stress, there are a few points worth remembering:

- Try to make eye contact frequently, so that the person feels acknowledged; although don't overdo it, as this

will be experienced by the other person as confront-
ational or aggressive, and by some Eastern cultures as
an invasion of privacy or as being rude.

- Try to have your eye levels equal, so that you are not
looking up at the other person as a child would (this
stance might trigger your 'inner child', who feels inferior or inadequate), or looking down, which could
feel patronising or threatening to the other person. (So,
if you are sitting at your desk and your boss walks up
to have a chat, stand up or invite him/her to sit down,
so that you are at the same eye level with each other.
Although towering over someone else can make you
seem more powerful, sitting down and looking up can
also be used to your advantage in certain situations, if
you want to appear vulnerable and gain sympathy.
These techniques are subtle, but have an unconscious
impact, and some people use them deliberately to gain
a psychological advantage.) Similarly, if you are communicating with a child, you instinctively know that
the best way for success and trust is to bend from the
knees, taking your whole body down, so that your
heads are at the same level.

- When shaking hands, remember that the strength or
weakness of your grip has an important impact on the
other person. Too strong a grip can feel threatening or
give the impression that you are trying to dominate.
Obviously, a limp handshake will convey messages of
weakness or lack of interest. So be aware of the effect
you are having, as it will colour the communication.

- Posture is also important in communication of all
kinds. A drooping body can convey a depressing message or that you are not at all on top of things.
Standing with your weight well balanced on the balls
of both feet and holding your body upright (by pulling
up from either side of your waist) can make you feel
more alive and in control, and will certainly transmit a
message of liveliness and alertness.

- Try not to stand or sit in postures that look defensive,
for example, with your legs crossed and especially not
with your arms folded across your body. Not only
does it make you look inaccessible and cut off, but

holding your body in this way builds up the muscle tension and sends alarm signals to your brain, which initiates the Fight or Flight Response.

- When thinking about entering a room for maximum impact, observe how a cat does this: it usually moves slowly, but purposefully into a room, then pauses for a moment to survey the scene, sensing whether this is friendly or dangerous territory. Having absorbed the information, the cat then makes directly, but gracefully, for the place it has chosen to be, perfectly in control of its movements and its timing.

- Be aware of the tone and volume of your voice. It's not what you say, it's the way that you say it, that conveys the largest part of the message. Breathe from your diaphragm and you will be calm and mellow, and you will sound in control. (See Chapter 3 for techniques.)

Your relationship with yourself

Perhaps the most important relationship in your life is the one you have with yourself, the one you can't get away from. If you don't like or love yourself, then it is usually very difficult to be in harmony with other people.

Many people have problems with self-acceptance, which creates much of their stress. Often, if they are helped to understand themselves more completely, they begin to accept themselves and therefore to value themselves more.

To improve your understanding of your personality, you may be helped by looking at the model of different personality types and the ways they function that was developed by Carl Jung. He maintained that people could be classified into four fundamental types depending on the way they orientate themselves and perceive the world: through feeling, thinking, intuition or their senses.

A 'thinking type' will perceive things from a logical, objective, intellectual and factual point of view. A 'feeling type' will experience people and situations subjectively: he will feel the atmosphere, the 'vibes', the emotions of others, and be strongly in touch with his own feelings in a situation. This type responds to people with warmth and caring, empathy and sympathy, but can be petulant and moody. An 'intuitive type' perceives the inner aspects of things, rather than the outer, and knows instinctively how to make something happen, how to motivate someone, what makes people tick and how things will turn out. Often this personality type is also visionary. The fourth personality type, those who experience things predominantly through the senses, must be able to touch, smell, see, hear or taste something. These people are pragmatic; they are at ease in all practical activities and are very down to earth – the exact opposite of the intuitive type.

Many misunderstandings in life arise out of the different ways these four personality types approach the world. For example, if you were to ask each type in turn to describe a person they had just met:

- The thinking type would say: 'She's very intelligent and obviously well read. I gather she was educated at a London comprehensive school and won a scholarship to Trinity, Cambridge. She would make a good diplomat; I can't think why she's chosen to be a librarian – seems a waste of her intellect.' Here, the focus is on the mental attributes and the facts of the woman's life situation.
- The feeling type would say: 'She is charming, great fun and obviously a sensitive woman. I liked her.' The observations are all about inner qualities and subjective observations.
- The intuitive type would say: 'She's obviously been hurt badly in life and protects herself with a charming manner. She may be successful now, but I have a hunch she'll end up lonely and impoverished.' This type 'sees' (but not with the physical eyes) more deeply into people and things, has flashes of insight and talks a lot about the future.
- The sensation type would say about the same woman: 'She's about 5 feet 4 inches (1.63 metres) tall, dark haired, expensively dressed and well groomed; she had a firm handshake.' The observations concern only what can be perceived through the senses.

Jung devised the diagram below to illustrate his hypothesis of the four functions:

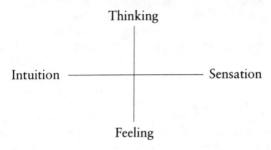

Jung recognised that if one function is dominant or uppermost, then the function at the opposite pole will be the weakest area for that person. So, a thinking type will be underdeveloped in his or her feeling function and an intuitive type will be weak in the sensation or practical function, and vice versa. When we misunderstand others, often it is because they are seeing things from the opposite pole to our own, or are explaining themselves in terms of their dominant function, to which we may be blind, or simply not comprehend.

Applying Jung's diagram to your own circumstances

Applying Carl Jung's theory may help you to understand yourself a little better, why you react the way you do, and why perhaps some of your communications and attempts to relate seem to miss the mark or just not connect in the way you intended. Nobody is solely one type to the exclusion of the others. We are all a mixture of types, though there is usually one that is our weakest point.

You may, for example, be an intuitive type with a sensation-type boss, which will usually mean that you each see things from completely opposite points of view and may frequently feel greatly misunderstood or misjudged, because the points you try to make are not grasped.

A friend recently described a frustrating conversation he had been having with an intuitive woman he knew by saying, 'It was like building a house with someone who wanted to put the roof on first!' The intuitive type takes it for granted that you've laid down the foundations, built the walls and so on. What they are always after is the realisation of the vision; they are not interested in the process required to get there.

A sensation-type boss will start off with the first necessary step and could stay on that spot for quite a time, getting all the details right. The intuitive type could blow a gasket waiting for the next step, and the one after, and the one after that ... If, however, these personality types understand what is going on between them, it could be a winning partnership rather than a frustrating one, because the strengths of each are the weaknesses of the other. The sensation type is not a visionary and therefore needs the intuitive person to create the picture of the successful end product; whereas, the intuitive person needs the practical application of the sensation type in order to get anywhere at all. The intuitive type needs to be grounded a little more firmly, and the sensation type needs to be helped to look further ahead.

Or, imagine a feeling-type boss with a thinking-type assistant who asks her boss: 'Would it be all right if I came in late on Monday morning, as I have to take my daughter to the dentist?' All the thinking-type assistant requires is a 'yes' or a 'no', maybe backed up by factual information; but the feeling-type boss would say something like: 'Oh dear, I did need you on Monday to go over that presentation I'm giving, and I had hoped you could accompany me to the board meeting at midday. But I suppose your daughter's teeth are important, so I'll just have to manage alone.' This answer is not really either a 'yes' or a 'no', just a lot of talk about the boss's own predicament, with an undertone of emotional blackmail.

Two people of a similar type will have a satisfying rapport and feel less irritation and frustration with each other, but on the other hand they may miss out on the opportunity to develop a broader view and an alternative way of handling situations that could be learned from attempting to see the strengths of the other polarity. The different types can complement each other if they appreciate each other's approach rather than assuming that one is right and the other is wrong. If you can understand your own dominant orientation, you may be able to explain yourself more clearly to others and understand better how they might be perceiving things. It can help in your interactions if you listen carefully to the language someone uses. It may explain where their dominant function is. For example:

- The thinking type cannot understand the subjective and emotional position of the feeling type and often thinks them a little 'wimpish' and too soft.
- If they say 'I feel' a great deal, instead of 'I think', you will know they are a feeling-dominated person, and it might help if you use the same terms back to them.
- The feeling type relates well to the intuitive type, but does not feel comfortable with the objective logic of the thinking type, finding this approach cold and unsympathetic.
- The intuitive type will say 'I know', 'I sense' or 'I see' quite a lot; they have an aura about them of being certain about things and how they will turn out – and they are usually right, although their attitude can be maddening. They often arrive at the right result, but usually can't tell you the process they went through to get there, because it is not logical.
- The sensation type will find this infuriating and will be unable to relate easily to the vagueness of the intuitive type. Nor does this type have much time for the imagination of the feeling type. For people who experience things mainly through their senses, life is about doing and getting on, and anything abstract, such as talk about feelings or looking at things symbolically or metaphorically – in other words, imaginatively – is unreal to them because 'It doesn't get you anywhere.'

It is not a question of which approach is right or better. No one type is better than any other; they are simply different. It is a question of being who you are. Of course, we all have expectations of others; but perhaps if we tried to expect a little less, and understand a little more, in the relationship with ourselves as well as others, everyone might feel a little less stressed.

> *This above all – to thine own self be true,*
> *And it must follow, as the night the day,*
> *Thou canst not then be false to any man.*
> Hamlet (Act I: Scene iii)

Chapter Eight

Stress and the Working Environment

E ach year millions of working days are lost through illness, much of it resulting from stress in the workplace. This chapter addresses the contributing factors that make a working environment unhealthy for its occupants and what effect these problems can have on you, followed by some positive, practical solutions that can be implemented even if you have only limited control over the physical aspects of your working environment. For those who work on their own, there are also suggestions about looking positively at isolation and how to capitalise on the advantages of being your own boss.

Improving your own environment

Problem:

Lack of air flow; air quality stale, too dry, too hot or cold; draughts.

Effect on you:
Sinus problems, colds, coughs, headaches, neck and shoulder pains (from tensing up against draughts or feeling too cold), chronic tiredness.

Solutions:
Air ionisers counteract stuffiness, keeping the air fresh and clear by charging it with a continuous output of healthy negative ions. Positive ions build up in the atmosphere as a result of central heating, air conditioning, cigarette smoke, overcrowding, general pollution and low barometric pressure. You can keep the air around you fresh and healthy by putting a small ioniser beside your desk or work space. In a large

open-plan office, a number of ionisers placed around the room would be helpful to everyone. Open windows as often as possible, even if air conditioning is operating or traffic noise and pollution will impinge for a while – there really is nothing to beat the flow of fresh(ish) air. However, if you cannot escape air conditioning, keep the temperature at about 19–23°C (66–73°F), and try to maintain a comfortable level of humidity. Central heating can also cause the atmosphere to dry out, so if the budget does not allow the purchase of a humidifier, you can put bowls of water above radiators and around your work space to increase humidity in an overly dry atmosphere; this is important, as you may become dehydrated if there is insufficient moisture in the air. Keep some bottled water in or near your desk or work station, and drink from it frequently to counteract dehydration, which can lead to drowsiness and lethargy; also, reduce coffee consumption, which is another cause of dehydration. Plants and vases of fresh flowers also contribute to the humidity, as well as breathing out essential oxygen into the environment; so the more plants around you, the better the air quality.

Problem:

Pollution from carbon monoxide, carbon dioxide, radon, ozone, dust, cigarette smoke; unappealing smells.

Effect on you:
Respiratory problems, sore throats, tension, fatigue, poor concentration.

Solutions:
Implement all of the above suggestions and burn pleasant-smelling incense or essential oils. Certain scents, chosen well, can be uplifting and stimulating to your mood and can assist clear thinking, as well as clearing and purifying the air. Most uplifting are: jasmine (sensual), rosemary (stimulating), rose (calming), lavender (soothing), lemon and all citrus fruits (stimulating and enthusing). Ventilation is especially important if there are chemical vapours in the atmosphere. Try to keep photocopiers and fax machines in a separate room, or screen them off to minimise their noise and chemical pollution.

Problem:

Fluorescent lighting; poor lighting; insufficient daylight.

Effect on you:
Headaches, skin blemishes (fluorescent light destroys vitamin A in the skin), eye strain.

Solutions:
Avoid fluorescent lighting if you possibly can, or buy full-spectrum bulbs. These simulate daylight by containing the full light-ray spectrum, including ultraviolet rays, which normal lights do not contain. They are more expensive, but will prove cost-effective in the long run by reducing health problems. (See Useful Addresses for stockists.) If your workplace is lit with fluorescent lights, then take the recommended daily dose of vitamin A, a daily cod-liver oil capsule, or drink organic carrot juice regularly (carrots absorb more nitrites and nitrates from the soil than any other vegetable). Buy yourself, or ask your employer to buy, an angle-poise lamp to minimise the need for overhead lighting and to provide adequate light directly onto your work to avoid eye strain.

Natural light is vital to us, as it regulates the levels of the hormone melatonin, which has powerful effects on sleep, mood and the reproductive cycle. Lack of daylight can be a serious problem for some people in the long, dull winter months, and the condition SAD (seasonal affective disorder) is now widely recognised amongst medical practitioners. The symptoms include depression, sleeplessness, poor concentration and carbohydrate craving. For more information on SAD, you should contact the SAD Association. (See Useful Addresses.)

Problem:

Overcrowding and noise; other people too close; other people's conversations distracting your concentration; telephones ringing, fax machines and photocopiers whirring; desk space too small; other desks too close; other people's belongings encroaching into your space; constant interruptions.

Effect on you:

Stressful emotions such as anger, frustration, irritation, which can lead to raised blood pressure, indigestion, breathing problems, headaches, tension, fatigue, aching muscles and a whole host of other stress reactions, feelings of powerlessness, despair and depression.

Solutions:

We all need a certain amount of space around us in order to feel comfortable. Psychological research has found that there are specific distances at which we need to keep other people, depending on our relationship with them (see p114). When we cannot maintain these distances, or have no control over them, we become uncomfortable. In overcrowded conditions, animals become fearful or vicious, and due to our fundamental need to control our own space, we have the same kind of instinctive reactions. So do not think it is neurotic or pretentious to demand sufficient space for yourself – it is normal and necessary for your wellbeing.

Untidiness and clutter can also make you feel overcrowded and uncomfortable, so try to keep a certain amount of order and tidiness around your work space, utilising stacking storage boxes or box files to contain clutter and paperwork. Space that looks ordered is usually more restful, so give attention to your visual environment. On the walls around your work area, put up posters or postcards of peaceful scenes, of paintings that uplift you or of places you have visited and enjoyed – anything that reminds you of a calmer dimension will help to buffer you against the unavoidable pressures and demands.

It is important to punctuate the technological and mechanised world with reminders of what is significant for you at the personal and human level. Remember that technology is there to serve us, not the other way round; it must never be allowed to dominate us or diminish the human dimension. Make your workspace beautiful as well as functional, and make sure that the human and personal aspect is not inadvertently banished from your environment, however small it may be.

Problem:

Other people's stress!

Effect on you:

Compounding any problems you may already have – it is so easy to 'catch' other people's tensions without realising it.

Solution:

Just practise refusing inwardly to take on other people's stress reactions. Learn to recognise when you are absorbing someone else's tension and distress, and create an imaginary boundary line between you and that person. Visualise their stress bouncing off the boundary, or floating over your head. Affirm to yourself which problems belong to them and which to you, so that you react only to yours. You can stay calm and relaxed even when those around you are worked up – just affirm to yourself that this is the case and practise the relaxation techniques covered in Chapter 3 regularly, so that you can slip into the Relaxation Response when you most need it.

Problem:

Bodily discomfort; badly designed furniture; unnatural static posture; too much repetitive work; insufficient breaks; not enough variety; too much time spent in front of VDU screens.

Effect on you:

The problems listed above can lead to a seriously disabling condition known as RSI (Repetitive Strain Injury) or Upper Limb Disorder, as well as less serious but debilitating chronic aches and pains in the arms, hands, back, neck and shoulders, in addition to headaches and eye-strain.

Solutions:

It is essential to have chairs that give proper support to our body structure and desks and worktops that are not too high or too low. Physical strain and tension are very stressful for the body, so it is important not to ignore pain or to take it for granted that it is just part of working life. Any pain in the body is a signal that something is wrong and it should be attended to.

Your chair:

A good chair will be designed so that all its components move independently, enabling it to be adjusted to suit your shape, size and height. It should fully support the spine, especially in your lower back. Placing a small cushion in the small of the back can give extra support, if you are suffering from backache. Specifically designed posture cushions are available from a number of sources. (See Useful Addresses.)

When sitting, both your feet should be able to rest flat on the floor. If your legs are dangling, this causes strain on your lower back and means that you need a footstool or support of some kind under your feet, so that they are resting on something. Your knees should be bent at an angle of about 90 degrees, so that your heels are resting just underneath your knees. Try not to cross your legs as this impairs circulation (exacerbating varicose veins) and twists the spine, which puts a strain on the back muscles. The seat depth should comfortably support your legs from hip to knee without putting pressure on the middle of the thigh.

There should be enough spring or give in the chair to support your body and eliminate shock through your spine. However, it should not be so soft that it allows your pelvis to sink into it. There should be a swivel and a five-castor base to allow the chair to move freely. Adjustable arm rests may be helpful, although they are not absolutely necessary.

Your desk/work station:
It is important that the height of your desk allows your forearms to be parallel to the floor while you are using a keyboard. This should be positioned to allow your wrists also to be kept parallel to the floor to avoid undue strain. Your wrists should be neutral while keying, not bending upwards, dropped or deviated inwards or outwards; all of those undesirable positions contribute to RSI and other disorders, such as carpal tunnel syndrome, tenosynovitis and tendonitis. When you are sitting at the desk, your elbows should be bent at about 90 degrees or just over and they should be in line with your shoulders. There should be sufficient room for you to put your legs comfortably under the desk.

The equipment on top of your desk should be arranged so that you avoid asymmetrical postures, i.e. the height of the VDU screen should be at eye level and directly in front of you, as should the keyboard. Joints should remain in as neutral a position as possible. The screen should be at an arm's length from where you are sitting. If your body is symmetrical, with your spine straight and head held straight, you will feel less fatigued and will minimise aches and pains, as you are not putting undue strain on the body.

If your work does demand a lot of screen work, take note of these additional pointers:

- Keep the screen clean.
- The screen brightness and contrast should be adjusted in accordance with lighting conditions. Glare and reflection must be minimised. Ideally, the screen should be positioned at a 90-degree angle to the light source. Lighting should be positioned to eliminate reflections from that source as well.
- Ensure that screen colours are not causing you eye strain. Avoid fluorescent multi-coloured screens.
- Avoid the colour white as much as possible, as it is the most reflective colour (i.e. white walls, white desks, white clothes, white paper).
- Be aware that glass panelling and the glass in picture frames also cause reflections.
- Document holders are very helpful when you are keying from copy, as they minimise the need for awkward movements of your head and eyes. The ideal one is hinged like an angle-poise lamp and can be positioned to the side of the screen at the same height and distance.
- Take care about all cables and flexes required for power to computers, printers, telephones etc. Cables should not encroach on leg space, and should be taped or bridged on the floor to avoid tripping.

All the ergonomic information opposite was supplied by Wendy Chalmers Mill from Interact Consulting at The Body Garage. This is a team of chartered physiotherapists specialising in work-related disorders; especially RSI or Upper Limb Disorder. See Useful Addresses. The information here is contained in her book *RSI: Repetitive Strain Injury* (Thorsons, 1994).

The ideal work station looks like this:

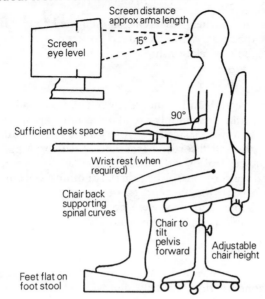

The ideal desk is arranged like this:

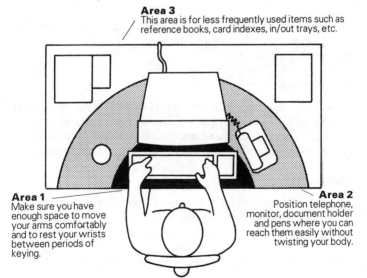

Area 3
This area is for less frequently used items such as reference books, card indexes, in/out trays, etc.

Area 1
Make sure you have enough space to move your arms comfortably and to rest your wrists between periods of keying.

Area 2
Position telephone, monitor, document holder and pens where you can reach them easily without twisting your body.

Different space requirements

As mentioned earlier, research has identified four different types of space at which we need to keep other people, depending on our relationship with them.

Intimate space

This is between 1 and 6 inches away from us, and usually only lovers and close family are allowed into this space. Any invasion of intimate space by anyone else causes great distress and even physical disorders, especially if it is prolonged and we have no control over the other person, as, for example, in a crowded train or bus. When there is nothing we can do to alter the situation, we tend to depersonalise it, looking through people as if they were not there, treating them as impersonal objects or behaving aggressively.

Personal space

This is between 6 and 18 inches away from us, and is the comfort zone for those we trust and with whom we are close emotionally, but not intimate. When this space is invaded by anyone outside those categories, they are transgressing our boundaries. We become stiff and tense, trying to hold them off with our body posture. Extroverts can usually tolerate more intrusion of their intimate and personal space than introverted types.

Social space

This is the distance between 18 inches and 4 feet away from us and is for more impersonal interactions, like interviews, business transactions and meetings, and for formal social occasions with people who are not close friends or family.

Public space

This is between 4 and 12 feet away from us, which is the sort of space that would feel comfortable if we were giving a lecture, for discussions, presentations, teaching and so on.

Understanding your spatial needs will help you to organise

your working environment to your maximum comfort. In some offices, desks are facing each other, which means you have someone talking and breathing directly into your personal space, even if there are computer screens separating you. One solution is to create more of a barrier between yourself and other colleagues by a strategic arrangement of plants, by putting a small bookcase at the edge of your desk or work-surface or by using acoustic screens, which are excellent for muffling other people's sounds. (See Useful Addresses.) Strategic placement of cabinets and floor-standing shelves are other ways of protecting yourself, if the room allows.

Avoiding interruptions

To keep interruptions to a minimum, avoid making eye contact with colleagues and resist looking up if an intrusion has occurred, whilst stating firmly that you cannot be disturbed, as you have a deadline to meet. If the other person is persistent, simply resist adding anything unnecessary to the conversation, and again, keep eye contact to a minimum. When the other person finishes speaking, remain silent. Do not allow yourself to be drawn into small talk. If you have your own office and want someone to leave, get up and begin to walk towards the door, using body language to indicate that the meeting is over; or make an ending statement like, 'Thank you for looking in, I'll get back to you later,' or 'Can you get back to me later?' Either way, make it very clear that this is the end of the interaction. If the other person tries to continue with the conversation or side-track you, then you may have to use the 'broken record' technique: this consists of repeating your last statement, such as 'I must get on with this report now, I'll get back to you later', as many times as necessary for the message to sink in. It is very effective.

Be firm about other people's possessions and work creeping into your space and about the noise levels you can tolerate. The ring of telephones can be set at a low volume, and windows should be double glazed if there is excess traffic noise outside. Carpeted floors will absorb more noise than linoleum or wood floors.

Be firm about both your physical and temporal boundaries. Be clear about how much time you are willing to give to a particular meeting or transaction, and don't allow yourself to be pushed beyond your deadline. This way you begin to control time and space, rather than feeling victimised by not having enough of either, and it frees up your energy. Learning how to be firm about your boundaries in many different situations will save you much unnecessary stress; blurred boundaries are one of the greatest sources of inner discomfort and distress.

Taking regular breaks

No matter how perfectly you position your body at your desk or work station, it is not natural for the human body to be kept in static postures for any length of time. Our bodies function best when they are kept moving. Take regular breaks and get up and walk around at least once every hour, and stretch your body regularly. (See Chapter 3 for stretches and movements you can practise while at work.)

Stretch your eye muscles by regularly focusing out into the distance or out of the window, or close your eyes and circle them round in both directions, then look up to the ceiling and down to the floor without tilting your head; move your eyes from side to side, to give the muscles a break.

Remember that after two hours of intense keyboard work mistakes become more frequent, so taking short 5–10 minute breaks will reduce your errors, as well as taking the physical strain off your body. During your break get up and walk around, stretch and yawn, perhaps go outside and breathe in some fresh air. Jog on the spot to deepen your breathing and to stimulate your circulation. Breaks also give your mind a rest and give you a different perspective on things; taking time to stand back is never time wasted because it can clear away a lot of tension and stress. Vary your tasks throughout the day so that you get a balance between sitting and being more active.

Static posture and its undesirable side effects are not only occupational hazards for people sitting at computer screens – they can be problems for musicians, train drivers, pilots, telephonists, people working on assembly lines or sitting for many hours at a check-out counter. Even Guardsmen on duty outside the royal palaces are allowed to rock unobtrusively backwards and forwards from heel to toe to introduce a little movement into their static working day. This stimulates their blood circulation just enough to ensure they do not pass out! Movement, good posture, breathing correctly and stretching out contracted and tense muscles will help to keep the body relaxed and de-stressed during the working day.

Working on your own

Many of the problems already covered in this chapter apply equally to someone working at home. If you have opted for this kind of situation, there are, however, specific stresses that you may experience.

The challenge of working on your own is to capitalise on the advantages, and a major one is that you are in control. You are the master of your environment, and you have the opportunity to create an atmosphere that is positive, creative and supportive to your productivity. How you achieve this will depend on your temperament and individual needs, but at least you have the opportunity to personalise your space in any way that is satisfying. You can have music playing if it does not distract you or you can break off to listen to the news or watch a favourite TV programme, so long as you can trust yourself to be disciplined about returning to work.

Problem:

Having to set up an environment that will serve your needs; creating a structure for effective work.

Solution:

It is important to recognise that working alone or from home is fundamentally a different ball-game involving different needs. The independence gained from working alone can turn into the stress of having to do absolutely everything yourself, and this can feel quite daunting after the novelty has worn off. You have to answer the telephone, respond to the door bell, put the dog out and make your own cups of tea and coffee, having remembered not to run out of milk – or paper, pens, light bulbs, stamps, envelopes, Sellotape, Jiffy bags, paper clips, and so on endlessly. The spread of tasks increases and the roles increase. Take all of this into account as you pace yourself during the working week.

You will have to decide on the best sort of timetable for producing the results you need, and it may be that the type of structure which operates in an office environment needs to be adjusted when you are working alone.

Because of the isolation of being on your own all day, you may need to take breaks from the silence at regular intervals, to go out and mingle with other people and be stimulated by their energy. Therefore, your timetable might start earlier, say at about 8.30 a.m., and you could then introduce a break at 11.30 a.m. and go out to shop or to the post office or the library. After spending a little time in amongst the crowds, you will probably have had all the human contact you need to make you appreciate your own blissful peace and silence.

Thus, another upside of working alone is that your routine can be more varied – in fact, the routine doesn't have to be routine. Some days you might simply go out for a walk to stretch and get some fresh air, and to make up for these breaks you can work later, when most office workers would be spending unproductive time commuting.

Problem:

Undefined boundaries; need for greater self-discipline.

Solutions:

To minimise frustrations, the division between work space and home space needs to be clearly defined. Unclear boundary lines cause a great deal of avoidable distress. Ideally, you should have a separate room for your work, but if this is not possible, then at least have clear divisions within the living space between work equipment and the things that belong to your home life. If you use certain rooms during the day for working or meeting with clients, be clear about when they revert back to being available for family or social use. Make sure members of your family are clear about these divisions and have had some say in the way they have been arranged – this ensures their goodwill, which is important in supporting you in your working endeavours. Clear time divisions are also important. Set definite times for beginning and finishing the working day, and be disciplined about sticking to them.

Self-discipline is an issue when working on your own. One has to be firm with oneself about getting started and about staying put when domestic or social interruptions threaten to distract from the task in hand. Just say to yourself, 'I am at the office and cannot deal with the window cleaner, or callers at the door, or children's demands for attention.' Then you can decide when you 'leave the office' and walk over the boundary line into home life again. However, while it is important to be firm with yourself about getting down to work, it is just as vital that you do not work excessively long hours just because you never actually physically leave the office. Make sure that you allow yourself sensible cut-off points.

Problem:

Storing your work equipment.

Solutions:

If you have to work on the kitchen table or the dining-room table, purchase some appropriate storage units for putting away your work things at the end of the day, when the table has to revert back to family use. If papers and working equipment are contained in this way, you will feel more ordered and organised, and you will be able to find them easily next day and slip comfortably again into the work frame.

Papers, books, pens, highlighters and so on scattered about or randomly balanced in wobbly, untidy piles all around the house are certain to cause you stress, anxiety and muddled thinking. You could buy attractive wicker or cane baskets to hold work items, or multi-layered trays, or a combination of both. Wallet-type files are very useful and can be clearly marked on the outside so that the contents are catalogued. Be imaginative about the storage items you choose, and be creative and artistic; this makes your environment stimulating and inspiring. It is easy not to bother if nobody comes into your space very often; but don't forget the very important person who comes into it every day – you. Make it attractive and supportive for that person.

Problem:

Isolation; lack of feedback from colleagues; too much silence and low energy in the atmosphere.

Solutions:

Isolation can be one of the major problems in working from home or in a separate small office. To counteract this, take occasional breaks by picking up the phone just to chat to a friend or colleague. This is not escapism or indulgence; the different perspective received from others is not to be under-valued and can prevent you from taking things too seriously, especially yourself. When you are alone for long periods it is very easy to get things out of perspective. The main problem can be that we become too critical of ourselves and too hard on ourselves; every little mistake is blown up out of all pro-portion. This, of course, can cause depression and low self-esteem; the lack of positive feedback – or any feedback – from colleagues can become eroding.

So take this aspect of working on your own into account and allow yourself some breaks from the solitary confine-ment, perhaps arranging regular lunch meetings two or three times a month. You also need to work harder at creating a social life outside of working hours when there is no social interaction during the day. Although a definite upside to being cut-off from others is that you are spared their bad temper, criticisms, moodiness or irritating habits, it is impor-tant to feel that you are still 'in the swim of things'.

Chapter Nine

Why Do Some People Thrive on Stress?

There are certain things to be learned from successful people about how to achieve to the maximum of one's ability or desire, and how to thrive while doing so. Research into why or how 'top' people cope with the enormous demands upon them has revealed some interesting common denominators – the first of these are known as the three Cs.

The three Cs

Control

Most successful people thrive on the demands or problems of their lifestyle rather than collapsing under the load partly because they have control over their lives or they perceive themselves as having control. This is encouraging and enabling, even when it goes hand-in-hand with tremendous responsibility. Having a high degree of control over most situations relieves feelings of distress, threat or helplessness and therefore reduces the amount of stress involved, and so more energy is available for a high level of performance. Also, when you feel sufficiently in control of your destiny, you can relax more often and take time off, which, of course, is sensible, healthy self-management.

Not having control, or perceiving yourself as having little control, is one of the greatest stresses we can face, and because of the negative consequences for health, avoidance of too many situations where you cannot control the situation or outcome may be wise stress management. Try to identify those areas where you do have control. You can then maximise the benefit of these situations by concentrating your efforts on these projects or areas. You should also frequently remind yourself that these are *positive* situations, which will in turn give you confidence to deal with more difficult areas.

If you do not have much control in your working life, make sure that you engage in your leisure time in activities where you can feel in control to a satisfactory degree; for example, by playing a sport regularly with a friend with whom you feel equal, developing your game or developing your artistic or musical abilities so that you feel more in control of your own talents and capabilities. Attending a self-defence class or practising meditation, tai chi or any of the martial arts can also give you a sense of control. Rather like the conductor of an orchestra, you can co-ordinate the many sides of yourself to function in the most satisfying way.

Even if you have achieved considerable seniority in the workplace, do keep a check on where you feel unfree, as this is where the stresses intensify, and try to find ways to gain more control. For instance, managers are typically seen as having a significant level of control, but this greatly depends on the hierarchical structure of the organisation: middle managers are often squeezed from above and below, and generally experience more stress than those who work under them, who are only pressured from above. However, in spite of having certain constraints on your control, you can de-stress yourself considerably by choosing consciously to accept those constraints. This choice of accepting the situation rather than resisting it gives you a feeling of autonomy, but it has to be a genuine choice with which you feel comfortable.

The one area where we can always have control is in our reactions to outer events and other people. We are always free to choose how we interpret something that happens, and how we then decide to react. Of course, it is not always easy to find the inner control that enables us to stand back and take a moment to reflect before we act or react. By practising the techniques that are given throughout this book (especially those covered in Chapters 3 and 5), you will become more centred and have more of a sense of not being out of control.

Most people who arrive at the top of their profession or career have found ways to take control as often as possible in all areas of their lives and to nurture the opportunities for increasing their areas of influence. When you take control even in little ways, such as deciding where you place your boundaries as far as other people's demands are concerned (see Chapter 8), your self-esteem and confidence grow, which gives you the courage to take more control of your life. Some people have a high degree of control at work but do not take sufficient control of their free time, thus they can feel anxious at weekends, when there is no structure. So manage your leisure time as well, not by being frantically busy, but by deciding what you want to do, when you want to do it and when to relax, instead of just drifting.

Some people become depressed on weekends, perhaps because of the lack of a framework or purpose. In my therapy sessions men often complain that at weekends they do what their families want and arrive back at work on Monday morning feeling un-nourished and unrefreshed. Women too can suffer if, for example, they put all their energy into directing their children's lives and activities, or focus excessively on supporting their partner's course through life, and give insufficient attention to controlling and directing their own lives and talents towards greater self-expression and fulfilment. We can all get tied up with trying to please others rather than ourselves, feeling increasingly stressed by attempting to be what other people want us to be.

Top people are usually true to themselves, value self-expression, have the courage to be who they are and are not too hung-up on trying to please others. This is very empowering. Being free from the constraints of others is a wonderfully stress-free experience. To be free, however, we have to take responsibility for not allowing ourselves to be put upon: if you capitulate to other people's expectations, who is responsible? Sometimes we restrict our own freedom unconsciously – and it is important to be clear about who is doing what to whom!

Many people frequently stress *themselves* with excessive constraints, such as, 'I must achieve more than anyone before has achieved in this position,' 'I must work longer hours than any of my colleagues or partners' or 'I am not good enough unless I constantly prove myself with virtuoso performances or saintly behaviour.' In other words, they set impossible goals for themselves and then become tyrannised by them. If you feel burdened by the demands upon you, remember who set them up in the first place. You have a choice: you can always say 'no'. Therefore, control is not only an issue in the outer world, it is an issue for our inner self as well. The sort of control where we burden, repress or constrain ourselves is quite different from positive, empowering control.

Positive control is not a constraint so much as an enabler, and should be understood as the kind of control wielded by the director of a play, not that of an autocrat. It is the power to direct, not to dictate. Take as much control as you possibly can in as many life areas as possible and see this as an opportunity to become more powerful in your own eyes, to become the director of your life: to do more, to become more, to do what you want to do and believe to be right.

Challenge

Another feature of successful people is that they see life's demands and problems as interesting or exciting challenges to be overcome, not as threats that may overwhelm them. Obviously, whether something is perceived as a threat or a challenge to your ingenuity depends on the resources you think, or feel, you have available. Nevertheless, the inner attitude with which you approach life is a very important resource, and this can be developed and strengthened. (See Chapter 5.) Try to work on seeing problems as challenges to be approached from a new perspective. Instead of saying, 'I have a problem', you could try saying, 'I have a puzzle to solve', and see if it makes a difference. The next time you feel threatened by a problem or difficult situation, think of it as a game you have to play – you may not always win, but what is most important is the enjoyment of the game. This attitude is what distinguishes the winners from the losers in life – winners enjoy playing the game and do not get too upset when they lose, because there is always another game to be played tomorrow.

Think of all the problems and difficulties that you encounter as a means to discovering your capabilities and creativity, your resourcefulness, your full potential. These challenges stretch us, and it is only when we are stretched that we discover what we can be and do. If we are not challenged by life, we might never know the extent of our ability, the wonder of all that we contain within ourselves.

Commitment

This final C is perhaps the most empowering of all. Leaders in life do not simply go to work to do their job or to earn their pay packet, they engage in whatever they do because of a commitment to a vision, a belief or a personal philosophy. It is a commitment to a higher ideal than simply earning one's living, and the vision or philosophy generally pervades the whole of that person's life, not just their work life. For example, Henry Ford had a vision of providing motorcars for all ordinary people and a strong belief that it could be done; he worked tirelessly and successfully at realising the vision. Many presidents, managing directors or CEOs of organisations have a vision for the whole company and what it stands for in the world. It is this kind of commitment that creates a company's culture, and just as organisations with a strong belief system or sense of mission running through them are generally more successful than ones that have no vision holding them together, the same is true for individuals. This sort of commitment fires and motivates people, giving them a purpose above and beyond mere survival, or even profit margins. In this committed state, one is not easily discouraged, and this commitment provides a stability in a person's life which is very calming. An unshakable belief keeps you on course when the storm clouds break and the waters become turbulent.

When you have this sense of commitment to whatever it is that you are working at – whether it is your career, your marriage, your local scout group, campaigning for the environment or bringing up your children – it feels less of a chore and more like a reason for living.

Approaches to life

Most successful people are usually successful at a number of things; they seem to nurture their different abilities and do not stagnate; they instinctively create balance in their lives. Another feature is that they generally enjoy life, having a sense of humour and enthusiasm which is delightful to be around – in other words, they have an 'attitude' – a positive approach to life. Similarly, successful stress management is a positive approach – a strategy for life.

In order to create such a strategy for life, it is necessary to develop some underlying guiding principles, to re-learn the ancient wisdom, common sense and the truths contained in old wives tales or the things that 'nanny' or wise grand-parents might have known. It seems that we have severed our connection with many old values as we rush to embrace all the new and wondrous scientific discoveries and techno-logical innovations. Now it is time to create a new approach to life that combines the best of the ancient and the new. We must start thinking for ourselves in a new way and stop buy-ing in to destructive and unhealthy concepts and ways of life.

Although we live in a changing world, we must make sure that the changes are beneficial. The best way to start with this mission is to refuse to be brainwashed into believing that something like stress is good for us when we know deep down that it is not. The greater the number of people who begin to live stress-free lives, the more the influences will rip-ple out, and the tide of rush, hurry, struggle, compete, destroy the planet in the name of 'greater profits for a few', strain, complain and so on will begin to turn. If it becomes unfashionable and unprofitable to promote a lifestyle that results in stress, rush, strain and struggle, then something healthier and more balanced may begin to take root.

You may be saying that nobody overtly advocates the stressful life, but so much of what is currently promoted as worthwhile necessitates most people spending huge amounts of their time running round the treadmill of nine-to-five, with very little energy or time left over to appreciate or enjoy whatever it is they are killing themselves to achieve!

We need to create a new wisdom, to avoid teetering con-stantly on the brink of exhaustion, irritation and strain by keeping a balance between 'doing' and 'nondoing'. As dis-cussed in Chapter 3, how we balance our lives is always sig-nificant, and if things are swinging out of control or we feel uncomfortable, distressed or strained, then the cause can usu-ally be traced back to a lack of the necessary sort of balance.

The drawing opposite is a way to help you visualise your life as a circle divided up into the separate areas of work, home, family life, social life, recreation and so forth. Instead of running round the outer rim of the circle from one life area to another, on a constant treadmill, return each time to a neutral point at the centre of the circle. This central position can be labelled 'me', which is the resting place – the non-doing position – between all the doing areas.

In order to balance 'doing' and 'nondoing', or action and replenishment, or being engaged and disengaged, you need to go out from the centre to one area of life and then return to the 'me' position – to become calm, relaxed, to stop and recharge, before going out into another section of your life. Each time you start from neutral and then return to neutral before moving on into another activity or life area. This protects you from becoming more and more tightly wound up and increasingly more overloaded with the pressures and agendas from each section of your life.

Each time you return to neutral, make a conscious effort to off-load the baggage you have been carrying: let go of physical tensions as well as the emotional and mental ones. You move into neutral, back in touch with yourself, and free yourself up to take on the next arena in your schedule.

You will have to be creative about how you bring this off-loading about, because your way of switching off has to be something that works for you and is suited to your temperament and personality type. What is essential, however, is that you accept the basic principle: that in order to keep balanced you cannot 'give out' all the time, you must 'take in' as well. How much you need to take in – to replenish – depends on your state at any given time, and on how much you have been 'giving out' or using yourself up, and for how long. Listen carefully to your inner self rather than silencing the voice that tells you to stop. This is what the 'me' position symbolises, the return to the source, the centre of your being. Below is a list of suggestions for getting to neutral, off-loading, unwinding, returning to 'being' rather than 'doing' and recharging. It is a gathering up of the many ways suggested throughout the book, plus some extra ones to try. You may only have a minute, so some things in the suggestion list only take a minute; some take five minutes, and some take longer, for when you have more time.

Suggestions for recharging energy levels – for getting to neutral before moving out again into demanding activities

1. Say to yourself 'STOP', become completely still (whether sitting or standing), let your breath out slowly, in a long, slow sigh, and pull your shoulders down. Take a slow breath in, low down in your diaphragm; then breathe out again slowly, and this time check that your arms and hands are relaxed and loose. Repeat this exercise twice.

2. Lie down for 30 minutes and go through the deep relaxation routine in Chapter 3 and on my accompanying tape.

3. Take a long, warm bath with soothing bath oils such as lavender, jasmine or rose. Don't have the water too hot, as this will stimulate rather than soothe.

4. Bathe by candlelight.

5. Sit down, let go all through your body and listen to a soothing piece of music for half an hour. This will switch you from your 'left brain' into your 'right brain', which is refreshing in itself.

6. Play some soothing music for yourself in the kitchen whilst preparing a meal at the end of a busy day.

7. If you only have a moment, close your eyes and imagine something very beautiful and uplifting. It could be your favourite flower, a rose, the first daffodil of Spring, a waterfall, a fountain or a mountain stream, a stone like a diamond, an emerald or a pink crystal, or a sunset – whatever is precious and beautiful. This will uplift you and help to put things into perspective.

8. To expand your mind and nourish your imagination: pin up or stick beautiful pictures or photographs around your workspace: beside your desk, on your computer, in the kitchen above your work surfaces, even in the car – wherever you can.

9. Copy out any sayings or quotations that have inspired you recently and put them up around your workspace or your home, to remind you of the whole picture, the larger dimension.

10. Laugh: find as many opportunities as possible during the day to do this, remembering that a sense of humour gives a sense of proportion and releases tension.

11. Try to give, or receive, at least seven hugs a day. Remember, just hugging the people close to you – family, friends – or gently touching them, can often say more than words, and can be much more effective than words.

12. Whilst you are relaxing, imagine a beautiful place, some where you would like to be, somewhere you would feel safe and calm – a sort of inner sanctuary. It could be a room, a garden or some holiday place that you love. Call this scene to mind often so it becomes familiar to you; then, when you feel stressed, strained, upset or that things are getting on top of you, call up this special place and rest in it for a moment or two to give a breathing space.

13. Remember that giving your full attention to another person or task is less tiring than giving half-attention to a number of things at once. Also, a family member or colleague will be satisfied with less time if they have your

full attention, rather than a distracted you, so this saves time in the long run.

14. Stop, stretch, yawn: between tasks, all through the day.

15. Take one thing at a time. Practise putting what you are not engaged in to one side. You could visualise putting into a large box all the things ahead of you waiting to be done. Then see yourself putting the box somewhere safe, to await your attention when the time arrives. Imagine taking one thing out of the box at a time to be attended to. This can stop you panicking about the myriad tasks all needing your attention.

16. Give yourself time to breathe. Check your breathing – has it become shallow, or are you holding your breath? Take five minutes to breathe calmly and slowly from your diaphragm, making sure that your out-breath is a little longer and a little slower than your in-breath.

17. Remember: when you control your breath, you control your life. (This does not mean control in the sense of altering the rhythm nature intended: see page 48.)

18. Don't get angry with yourself – it is a terrible waste of energy.

19. Don't blame yourself – or others – it does not get you, or anyone else, anywhere constructive.

20. Do love yourself, and go through a mental check list of all your qualities and talents many times a day. First thing in the morning, at your coffee break, at your lunch break, before the evening activities begin and, especially, last thing at night after you get into bed. Appreciate yourself and reassure yourself that you are doing your best.

Extra suggestions specifically for parents

1. Sit down with your child, or children, and read them a story when you feel exhausted. This keeps them occupied, but gives your body a rest. Better still, lie on the sofa and have them lie next to you – this unwinds everyone; and, with a bit of luck, they might even fall

asleep for a while and so give you a chance to nod off! Failing that, try inventing a story, as this saves you from having to balance the book and focus outwardly, and, by being imaginative, you will move from your 'left brain' into your 'right brain', which will in itself refresh you.

2. Another imaginative and refreshing 'right brain' activity is to draw with your children. Lie on the floor and draw using crayons and large sheets of paper. This will allow you to rest while keeping the family happy.

3. Listen to music with your children, as this puts everyone into their 'right brain': again very restorative.

4. Sit down (even for just half an hour) and watch a favourite television programme with the children, this creates good 'bonding' and sharing, and gives you a rest. If you have been out at work all day, this will switch off your mind from the day's agenda, helping you to relax into the home atmosphere.

5. If noise levels are driving you mad – particularly when travelling with children in the car – you could suggest a sponsored silence. Offer a reward to whoever can be silent the longest.

6. Get the family to do a gentle exercise programme to-gether – have fun with it, don't take it too seriously. You could buy an exercise video to guide you and use it to ease tempers and tensions. Just doing fun things together can de-stress families and create goodwill and positive bonding.

Chapter Ten

Going to a New Place

This final chapter explores a further dimension that will almost always work to de-stress you when nothing else seems to provide any relief. This dimension is within each of us. It is sometimes called the 'Transpersonal Self', the 'Higher Self' or the spiritual dimension of our being.

From this place we connect with another way of perceiving both the inner and outer worlds, of achieving a greater sense of peace and equanimity. It is an understanding and feeling from which many of us have somehow become separated. It is like a room inside you that has been shut up and forgotten about, but which contains incredible treasures. If you can enter it and operate from there, the experience will create a different framework for your life. You will find you have more resources than you realised. In fact, everything will look slightly different.

This process relates to something I have spoken about a number of times throughout the book: that stress management can be seen as a question of perspective. If we can change the perspective, then everything changes: the goal posts are moved, as it were.

The Transpersonal Self rises above and beyond the everyday, ordinary personality. It is the part of us that relates to and identifies with the highest ideals and standards: it could also be called the Altruistic Self, and could be seen as the polar opposite of being selfish or self-centred.

From this perspective, you evaluate your experiences very differently. In the ordinary personality, the ego is very self-important, takes everything personally and puts itself always in the centre of the picture; whereas the Higher Self puts ideals first and understands the transformative power of unconditional love.

This way of seeing and behaving can give one an inner calm that mitigates and protects against outer stresses. From this place it is impossible to get too angry, resentful, bitter or vindictive. From here you see that everything has a purpose, even if you cannot fully understand the purpose at this moment. You take the longer view, you make the most charitable interpretation of actions and events and you exercise tolerance. You recognise that we are all imperfect, and this allows you to let go, which in turn brings emotional relief and a release from tension. This viewpoint restores equilibrium and is the source of all that we yearn for when we feel stressed: peace, silence, stillness, joy, wonder, bliss and awareness of our universal oneness with all that exists.

I am sure you recognise the experience: the sudden expansion of your consciousness, the opening of your heart, the desire to do wonderful things, to be a better person.

It is the magical, mystical, other-worldly dimension to which children relate so naturally and which adults seek to rediscover. It is a part of ourselves from which we have become estranged, but which, sometimes unknowingly, we search for: through romantic films, exotic holidays, chocolate, sex, alcohol, drugs, fast cars, glamorous clothes. But the sublime experience is not to be found in another lover, a new house or somewhere in the Caribbean: that half-glimpsed and dimly remembered feeling of joy, illumination, expansion, sparkling beauty and wonder is actually right here, right now, under our noses all the time. We just don't usually have the eyes to see – until something expands our consciousness and causes us to wake up. This is what Wordsworth alluded to when he wrote: 'Our birth is but a sleep, and a forgetting...'.

There are many different paths to this place, so you need to be alert for that which might assist you. For example, when I was a young girl and would get upset with someone or angry about something, my very wise father would say, 'Rise above it, darling.' It was only when I was much older that I began to understand how helpful that advice was for my happiness and emotional health. It gave me somewhere else to go. Now, I say it to myself whenever something threatens to overwhelm my equilibrium. This is a choice available to everyone: to rise above a problem, to go to another place, another level.

Watch out for the many signposts to and reminders of the higher level from which to view things. You can come across them in the most unlikely places, in the most unexpected ways. Many people who are too busy 'getting on' miss them all the time. You have to take a moment or two to stop, look and listen...and then listen again.

So look for it, be awake to it, be receptive to it at all times and in all places: find the magic, the mystical experience. Remind yourself that another dimension exists behind the obvious one. Go there, rest there, smile from there, love from there (yourself, at least, even if nobody else!).

I believe a great deal of the stress we experience is due to the fact that we remain out of touch with this dimension for most of our day and then attempt a quick fix: we brush with it for a short while in lovemaking, when we read to our children or in a few hours of worship. But we need to take it back from those few moments into more and more of our day. Why allow yourself to constrict, diminish, seize up with rage, shrivel up with fear?

Even if you have never directly experienced the dimension of the Higher Self, most people do have a vague sense, almost a memory, of somewhere 'other' or of something 'beyond' their ordinary, everyday existence.

Ask yourself:

- What will take me there?
- What has taken me there in the past?
- Where is it?
- What is it really?

Then practise these techniques:

- If you are in a stressful situation, remember how you felt walking on the beach, or after lovemaking, or looking out to sea on holiday, and bring that expanded feeling into the situation. Remember, you are always free to choose what you feel. Go to that place where you feel easy, relaxed, uplifted, generous, carefree.

- For some people, it may be music that transports them beyond their everyday concerns. When listening to music, give it your full attention and disregard mundane thoughts that attempt to bring you back down to earth, just listen for a while, and allow your consciousness to expand.

- For others, it may be paintings or sculpture that remind them of something 'above' or 'beyond'. Just stay with the experience as long as possible – it is the counterpoint to the everyday and ordinary. Stay in the extraordinary and be refreshed.

- This dimension could be experienced whilst reading poetry or prose, or a self-help book, such as this, which affirms your inner knowledge. Again, just feel yourself expanding to your full stature.

- Whilst walking in the countryside you might be transported by the beauty and reassuring presence of the natural world. Often, when one is surrounded by Nature, one has a sense of another force in operation, of something beyond the visible world that informs and animates the tangible – of what could be called the 'life force' or the living Spirit.

    Dr Hans Selye, one of the great pioneers in the understanding of stress (see Chapter 1), wrote in his book *The Stress of Life*: 'The most harmonious and mysterious creations are those of Nature; and to my mind, it is the highest cultural aim of the professional scientist to interpret that so that others may share in their enjoyment ... there is an equanimity and a peace of mind which can be achieved only through contact with the sublime.'[1]

- Watching a sunset, walking on a beach, sailing or mountain climbing may suddenly open you up and momentarily make you more aware; though it can happen in the most unlikely places. For the writer C. S. Lewis, it happened whilst he was sitting on a bus and he wrote a book about it titled *Surprised by Joy*. (See Suggested Further Reading.)

- Dance, exercise, martial arts, archery, playing darts, singing or chanting may take you there, because physi-

---

[1] Copyright information as given previously.

cal concentration, like meditation, opens the channel for the reconnection to be made.

- This other dimension can, of course, be deliberately sought out through deep relaxation, meditation or prayer, or through many different rituals of worship, all of which have as their main purpose the awakening of the practitioner to other levels of experience.

It is interesting to note that the word 'religion' means 'to re-connect': worth thinking about, perhaps. The truth, as I see it, is that religion is a framework, or a ritual, which is intended to enable us and assist us in getting back in touch with our total nature, which is spiritual as well as material.

These are just a few of the ways. Turn to them, or to others, as often as you can to create balance and perspective in your inner and outer worlds. There are many paths to the top of the mountain.

It is a very personal matter, finding a route to an expanded perspective. But whatever it is that uplifts you, that transports you to a higher level, do return to it often: to remind yourself of the 'other' place, to reassure yourself, to reconnect with an expanded personal universe. When you are in this place, all the things that stress and distress you will take on a different look, a different shape, a different hue. You will find everything easier to deal with from here. Nothing looks quite so daunting, nothing seems quite so overwhelming – because you experience your power to overcome, and to respond with love.

This is the level of *unconditional love* and when we love unconditionally, we connect with the divine that exists in all of us – you can't get much bigger than that!

So link in to this dimension through the means I have mentioned or through whichever way works for you, and remind yourself often that there is always another place to go, another way to see. Remind yourself, too, of the relative nature of most things in the mundane world: much of what we agonise over really isn't worth the effort. Put your efforts into the important things, and you will be richly rewarded.

In the words of Rabindranath Tagore: 'Do not cry when the sun goes behind the mountain, for your tears will prevent you from seeing the stars.'

Chapter Eleven

Implementing the Twelve-Point Plan and Creating the New Agenda

Below is a stress management check-list, set out as a Twelve-Point Plan: this is your agenda for creating a new approach to the stress of life.

I have drawn together, in a quick reminder list, the most essential strategies necessary for keeping on top of life's stressors as given throughout this book. When stress is getting the better of you, read through this list and note which points you are not managing successfully, or which ones you may be neglecting altogether. Then, turn to the appropriate chapter and re-read it carefully, noting down as you go which suggestions you need to implement.

Purchase a special notebook for this ongoing exercise; carry it around with you to remind yourself of what needs to be worked on, and to note down any sudden insights about what you are doing that may be contributing to your daily stress. These may only be little things, but they can soon add up to stress overload, or they may be hugely overwhelming factors that need attention. For instance, you may suddenly realise that every time you get into your car you not only grasp the steering wheel, but you clamp your teeth together as well! So you would create a section headed 'driving' and then write: 'Do not clench teeth when driving'. You may become aware that you are always short-tempered when you arrive home in the evening, and that this is a contributing factor to the lack of harmony in your home life, so you would write: 'Let the tensions go before walking through the front door, increase the perspective, appreciate my home and family'.

This notebook, therefore, gradually becomes the New Agenda for your new approach to your life. I hope it will become an important companion, along with this book, as you begin to construct the new, creative, de-stressed way of living for yourself.

Be as specific as you can in noting down each important insight. A systematic way to work with it could be the following: each time you react in a way that lets you down, or when something happens which upsets you or stresses you, take up your New Agenda notebook and write down:

1. What happened
2. What you did
3. What the result was
4. What you would have liked the result to be
5. What you need to do next time to get that result

Then work down The Twelve Point Plan to discover which aspects of yourself, or of your life, you are not managing successfully enough, or which point you need to implement to get your desired result.

Let me explain more fully: suppose you lost your temper and shouted at someone who is important to you. The result was that the other person also lost his or her temper and shouted back, harsh words were exchanged and you both walked away feeling great antipathy and hostility. The result you would have liked was for the misunderstanding to have been clarified positively, for some agreement to have been reached, and for each person to feel that a step forward had been taken. What do you need to do next time to get the result you want? The obvious answer is not to lose your temper, to control yourself. But that is not the answer! In order to answer the question you have to ask yourself another question: 'Why did I lose my temper?' Losing your temper was a symptom, not a cause. So you must always look behind the symptom to find what caused it.

What caused you to lose your temper could, of course, be many things; but let's suppose that in being honest with yourself, you realise it was because you were feeling unloved, unappreciated and generally over-stretched. First, you must take responsibility for those feelings, for the state you are in. Then, refer to the Twelve-Point Plan. Search down it until you come to a point that relates to your problem: for example, you would probably first look at Number 1: Are you failing to say 'No' when you should? Next, you might consider Number 5: Are you failing to take responsibility for looking after yourself? You might need to implement Number 6 as well. Do you see how the New Agenda works? You note down the action needed to reduce your feelings of stress, and everything else flows from that. You see, the New Agenda is written by you. It, together with these twelve essential points, can help you begin to live in a happier and better managed relationship with the stress of life.

The Twelve-Point Plan

1. Manage the interface. Be in control of what interacts with you. Maintain your boundaries. Give yourself permission to say 'No' or 'Not now': create an assertive vocabulary and develop the social skills for using it tactfully, and believe in your right to do so. (See Introduction.)
2. Keep a constant check on the number of changes you are dealing with and avoid making any unnecessary changes when you are stressed. Remember, you can only cope with a certain amount of change at any one time. (See Chapter 1.)
3. Balance tension and relaxation: doing and nondoing. Take the pressure off yourself regularly. Half an hour of deep relaxation re-energises you, so you have more energy to spend later. (See Chapter 3.)
4. Use the Relaxation Response more often than the Stress Response. Try not to switch on the Fight or Flight mechanisms, as they wear you out. (See Chapters 2 and 3.)
5. Take good care of yourself. Acknowledge your needs. Feed your soul and inspire your spirit. (See Chapter 4.)
6. Balance work and play. Take time off from your problems and seek out people who care for you and who give you positive feedback about yourself. Remember, laughter is one of life's greatest healers: a sense of humour gives a sense of proportion. (See Chapter 7.)
7. Nurture your relationships. Develop supportive networks. Accept yourself. Be yourself. (See Chapter 7.)
8. Eat well to support yourself. Food and drink are the raw materials your body uses to renew itself. (See Chapter 6.)

9. Think positively. Think about what you want to make happen, and how you want to be. Practise positive visualisations and positive affirmations. (See Chapter 5.)

10. Create a healthy and positive environment, at home, in the office, or wherever you work. (See Chapters 3 and 8.)

11. Remember the secrets of successful people, the three Cs: control, challenge, commitment. When stressed, try to gain as much control over events as possible, or focus on the areas that you can control, and try to accept the rest. See problems as challenges to your creativity and ingenuity, not as threats. Make a total commitment to whatever you engage in, find a higher purpose or an altruistic reason for your endeavours and you will remove the strain. If you commit your total being, everything is easier than when a part of you is pulling back. (See Chapter 9.)

12. When things seem at their worst, or you feel most stressed, rise above it! Practise becoming still and connecting with the peace and silence that lie behind the noise and rush. (See Chapter 10.)

When you use this check-list together with your New Agenda workbook, you become more truly the creator of your life; you strengthen your personal power. Your New Agenda notebook will eventually contain all the information you need for your life to be lived the 'New' way: the way that brings greater joy, satisfaction and success, and less strain, struggle and stress, in all aspects of your life.

I have presented many thoughts to guide you and I have shown you many ways to get you to the best possible place: you just have to do it! You are the one who is responsible for you, and taking responsibility for yourself and your life gives you freedom.

Enjoy reducing your stress – enjoy feeling great. Enjoy being the powerful, creative, happy, unique individual you were born to be. Enjoy the interesting journey of life. Enjoy yourself. Be Yourself.

Useful Addresses

Aleph One Ltd
The Old Courthouse, Bottisham
Cambridge CB5 9BA
For relaxometers and bio-feedback machines, also books and cassettes on stress management, relaxation and behavioural problems.

British Wheel of Yoga
1 Hamilton Place, Boston Road
Sleaford, Lincs NG34 7ES
Send SAE for details of yoga courses throughout the UK.

The Body Garage
Interact Consulting, 46 Kingsway
London WC2B 6EN
This team of chartered physiotherapists, massage therapists and ergonomists treat, and advise on preventing, work-related injuries.

Centre for Transpersonal Psychology & Transpersonal Perspectives
7–11 Kensington High Street
London W8 5NP
Offers a series of introductory and advanced workshops; a referral network is also available.

Cruse
126 Sheen Road, Richmond
Surrey TW9 1UR
Bereavement counselling.

FSL
Unit 1, Riverside Business
Centre, Victoria Street, High
Wycombe, Bucks HP11 2LT
Full-spectrum light bulbs and tubes.

The Hale Clinic
7 Park Crescent
London W1N 3HE
The Clinic has over 100 practitioners in a wide range of complementary therapies, and also houses a nutrition centre, supplying vitamin and nutritional supplements, and a library/bookshop/education centre.

Inter County
8 Ascot Industrial Estate, Icknield
Way, Letchworth SG6 1TD
For acoustic screens.

Posturite (UK) Ltd
PO Box 468, Hailsham
East Sussex BN27 4LZ
For posture cushions, ergonomically approved furniture, anti-glare filters, document holders and other office accessories.

Relaxation For Living Trust
Foxhills, 30 Victoria Avenue
Shanklin
Isle of Wight PO37 6LS
Publishes leaflets,audio tapes, books and videos covering stress, relaxation and daily living. Send large SAE for information and a list of relaxation and stress management courses in the UK.

SAD Association
PO Box 989 Steyning BN44 3HG
Send SAE for information on seasonal affective disorder, also prices and hire charges for light-emitting boxes to counteract it.

Sivananda Yoga Vedanta Centre
51 Felsham Road
London SW15 1AZ
Courses for all levels of yoga ability, also on meditation, positive thinking and developing will power.

The Society of Teachers of the Alexander Technique
20 London House, 266 Fulham
Road, London SW10 9EL
Teach correct use of the body to dispel tension and strain. Send SAE for directory of practitioners.

Westminster Pastoral Foundation
23 Kensington Square
London W8 5HN
Counselling organisation for all kinds of problems.

Suggested Further Reading

Bishop, Beata, *A Time to Heal*, Penguin, 1996.
Chalmers Mill, Wendy, *RSI: Repetitive Strain Injury*, Thorsons, 1994.
Cousins, Norman, *Anatomy of an Illness as Perceived by the Patient*,
    Bantam, 1981.
Covey, Stephen R., *The 7 Habits of Highly Effective People*,
    Simon & Schuster, 1992.
Dalton, Katharina, *PMS: The Essential Guide and Treatment Options*,
    HarperCollins, 1995.
Diamond, Harvey and Marilyn, *Fit For Life*, Bantam, 1985.
Fromm, Erich, *The Art of Loving*, Thorsons, 1995.
Gelb, Michael, *Body Learning: An Introduction to the Alexander
    Technique*, revised edition, Aurum Press, 1994.
Goleman, Daniel, *Emotional Intelligence*, Bloomsbury, 1996.
Grant, Doris, *Food Combining For Life*, Thorsons, 1995.
Harris, Thomas and Amy, *Staying OK*, Pan Books, 1986.
Hay, Louise L., *You Can Heal Your Life*, Eden Grove Editions, 1988
Hendrix, Harville, *Getting the Love You Want*, HarperCollins, 1990.
Hewitt, James, *Complete Relaxation Book: A Manual of Eastern and
    Western Techniques*, Rider, 1989.
Jeffers, Susan, *End the Struggle and Dance With Life*,
    Hodder & Stoughton, 1996.
Jeffers, Susan, *Feel the Fear and Do It Anyway*, Arrow, 1991.
Jung, C. G., *Modern Man in Search of a Soul*, 2nd edition, Routledge, 1997.
Lewis, C. S., *Surprised by Joy*, Fount, 1977.
Lewis, Thomas, *The Soldier's Heart and the Effort Syndrome*,
    Shaw and Sons, 1918.
Nixon, P. G. F., 'An appraisal of Thomas Lewis's effort syndrome' in
    Quarterly Journal of Medicine, vol. 88, 1995, pp 741–47.
Nixon, P. G. F., 'The grey area of effort syndrome and hyperventilation:
    from Thomas Lewis to today' in *Journal of the Royal College of
    Physicians of London*, vol. 27, no. 4 October 1993, pp 377–83.
Peck, M. Scott, *The Road Less Travelled*, Arrow, 1990.
Rowe, Dorothy, *Beyond Fear*, HarperCollins, 1987.
Rowe, Dorothy, *Depression: The Way Out of Your Prison*, 2nd edition,
    Routledge, 1996.
Skynner, Robin and Cleese, John, *Families and How to Survive Them*,
    Mandarin, 1990.
Trickett, Shirley, *Coming Off Tranquilisers and Sleeping Pills*,
    Thorsons, 1990.
Trickett, Shirley, *Irritable Bowel Syndrome and Diverticulosis*,
    Thorsons, 1989.
Weekes, Claire, *Self Help for Your Nerves*, Thorsons, 1995.

Healthy & Unhealthy Lifestyle Habits

Cut out and keep this page and keep it with you to remind yourself of ways to monitor/avoid stress.
The Twelve-Point Plan is repeated overleaf.

HEALTHY

- ✔ Regular exercise/movement
- ✔ Healthy diet
- ✔ Sufficient sleep
- ✔ Relaxation skills
- ✔ Balance between work and recreation
- ✔ Moderate alcohol consumption: for pleasure not need
- ✔ Sense of humour
- ✔ Ability to lose gracefully
- ✔ Ability to win gracefully
- ✔ Realistic goals
- ✔ Healthy finances
- ✔ Good support systems
- ✔ Satisfying occupation
- ✔ Self-esteem
- ✔ Kindness to oneself and others
- ✔ Managing stress
- ✔ Taking responsibility for your happiness

UNHEALTHY

- ✘ Sloth/sedentariness
- ✘ Unhealthy diet
- ✘ Insomnia
- ✘ Tension
- ✘ Workaholism
- ✘ Excessive dependence on alcohol and other poisons
- ✘ Humourlessness/anger
- ✘ Resentment of others' successes
- ✘ Arrogance/superiority
- ✘ Unrealistic goals
- ✘ Poorly managed finances
- ✘ Poor support systems
- ✘ Unsatisfying occupation
- ✘ Low self-esteem
- ✘ Punishing oneself (and having nothing left for others)
- ✘ Out of control
- ✘ Blaming others for your unhappiness

The Twelve-Point Plan

1. Manage the interface. Be in control of what interacts with you. Maintain your boundaries. Give yourself permission to say 'No' or 'Not now'.
2. Keep a constant check on the number of changes you are dealing with and avoid making any unnecessary changes when you are stressed. Remember, you can only cope with a certain amount of change at any one time.
3. Balance tension and relaxation: doing and nondoing. Take the pressure off yourself regularly.
4. Use the Relaxation Response more often than the Stress Response. Try not to switch on the Fight or Flight mechanisms, as they wear you out.
5. Take good care of yourself. Acknowledge your needs.
6. Balance work and play. Take time off from your problems and seek out people who care for you and who give you positive feedback about yourself.
7. Nurture your relationships. Develop supportive networks. Accept yourself. Be yourself.
8. Eat well to support yourself. Food and drink are the raw materials your body uses to renew itself.
9. Think positively. Think about what you want to make happen, and how you want to be. Practise positive visualisations and positive affirmations.
10. Create a healthy and positive environment, at home, in the office, or wherever you work.
11. Remember the secrets of successful people, the three Cs: control, challenge, commitment. When stressed, try to gain as much control over events as possible. See problems as challenges to your creativity and ingenuity, not as threats. Make a total commitment to whatever you engage in, find a higher purpose or an altruistic reason for your endeavours and you will remove the strain.
12. When things seem at their worst, or you feel most stressed, rise above it! Practise becoming still and connecting with the peace and silence that lie behind the noise and rush.